UNSOLVED

SCIENCE

This edition first published in 2016 by
New Burlington Books
The Old Brewery
6 Blundell Street
London N7 9BH
United Kingdom

ISBN 978-0-85762-456-7

Conceived, designed, and produced by
Quid Publishing
Part of The Quarto Group
Level 4 Sheridan House
114 Western Road
Hove BN3 1DD
England

www.quidpublishing.com

Design and illustration by Michael Lebihan

Manufactured in China

UNSOLVED

SCIENCE

ENIGMAS THAT HAVE PUZZLED
THE GREATEST MINDS

BILL PRICE

NEW BURLINGTON

CONTENTS

INTRODUCTION

Nothing in science can ever be said to be fully resolved; we just know more about some things than others. It advances because scientists maintain a sceptical attitude and are prepared to challenge even the most strongly held beliefs and opinions. The basic method is to formulate a hypothesis then test it by experiment and observation, so that a conclusion can be drawn about its validity. It is then ripped to shreds by other scientists, and, if it survives intact, science has advanced. If not, we have learnt that this approach was wrong, and scientists can move on to look for another solution.

Since the modern scientific method began to become established in the seventeenth century, remarkable advances have been made in our understanding of ourselves, the world around us and the universe in which we live. This body of knowledge is one of our greatest intellectual achievements, but it is a truism often repeated that the more we learn, the more we realise how much we have yet to know. Over the course of this book, we take a look at some of those areas of science that have proved to be particularly resistant to our attempts to understand them and, on occasion, have got us completely foxed. In neuroscience, for instance, we struggle even to describe our own consciousness, let alone explain how it works, while cosmologists have not the slightest idea what dark energy is, despite the fact that it makes up two-thirds of the mass of the entire universe.

Not all of the examples covered here are quite as intractable, though all of them have scientists scratching their heads. To introduce a little order in what might otherwise become a turbulent system (something we can't describe either) the book is divided into five sections, each concerning one of the main fields of science. So, we begin by looking at life itself in the biological sciences, before moving on to see how our knowledge of ourselves has been applied in medicine and neuroscience. We then consider the ground beneath our feet, with the Earth sciences of geology and geophysics, and, from there, we take on physics and

Left: Centaurus A, one of the closest galaxies to Earth, has been extensively studied for clues about black holes, the big bang and antimatter.

chemistry – those heavyweights of the physical sciences. Then we draw to a close by gazing up at the stars, trying to understand the universe through the study of astronomy and cosmology.

Our main concerns here are with the natural sciences, but science does not occur in a vacuum – even if some scientists behave as if it does – so we have to put up with the occasional intrusion of the likes of mathematics, economics, politics and the social sciences. Since science itself often refuses to fit into convenient boxes, we also end up with physics invading the cosmology section, and both biology and chemistry appearing almost everywhere.

These days, research is usually conducted by teams of scientists from many different disciplines. This reflects the complicated nature of the problems they are tackling. Often, making an advance in one field uncovers a whole new level of complexity. This is the cutting edge of science, and here it is at its most exciting and, at times, most frustrating. This is also the focus of this book – where science is advancing rapidly, or is stuck on the rocks of an apparently unsolvable problem. No one book could hope to cover all of the unanswered questions in science, but by taking examples from across the range, we get a perspective of some of its most notable problems – in the process, shedding some light on the vast body of knowledge we already possess, and indicating what we may discover in the future.

BIOLOGICAL SCIENCES

To begin at the beginning, we start our survey of the unsolved problems in the biological sciences with a look at some of the theories that have been proposed over the years to explain the origin of life on Earth. Charles Darwin was aware that spontaneous generation, a theory going all the way back to Aristotle, was not correct, though he could not come up with a better solution himself. Since Darwin's day, our knowledge of the biological sciences has expanded enormously, but we still have not been able to pin down where it all began.

The search for the origin of life leads us to consider what caused the Cambrian explosion – when a huge diversity of complex life-forms evolved in a relatively short space of time – before we move on to the extinction of the dinosaurs, which opened up the way for the rise of the mammals. We then consider some of the other mysteries of the biological sciences, beginning with migrating animals and their ability to navigate over great distances, and moving on to the ocean floor, the last great undiscovered region of the Earth. At the end of this chapter, we take a look at how the genetic code contained within our DNA is expressed, and what science can do to help with the world's rising human population, which is set to increase dramatically over the course of the next three decades.

Left: Dr Stanley Miller synthesising organic compounds in his famous 1953 attempt to replicate conditions for the origin of life on Earth.

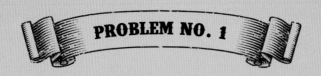

HOW DID LIFE ON EARTH BEGIN?

Field: Biochemistry, microbiology, genetics, cell biology
Location: Somewhere on Earth

One of the key unanswered questions in biology, and in science as a whole, concerns how life on Earth began. As far as we know, our planet is the only place in the universe where living organisms exist.

To examine how life on Earth occurred, we have to unravel abiogenesis. This is the process by which inanimate, inert atoms and molecules come together to produce complex organic molecules that demonstrate the abilities to replicate and sustain themselves – two of the principal features of life.

Until the mid-nineteenth century, the prevailing theory on the origin of life was spontaneous generation, which suggested that living organisms developed from inanimate non-living material without any outside influences – arising, for instance, out of mud or dust. The theory can be traced back to the ancient Greek philosopher Aristotle in the fourth century BCE, and did not come under serious scrutiny until the development of the microscope in the late seventeenth century led to the discovery of bacteria and other microorganisms.

FROM ARISTOTLE TO PRIMORDIAL SOUP

Spontaneous generation was not decisively disproved until 1859, when Louis Pasteur conducted an experiment in a sealed flask that clearly showed microorganisms could not arise spontaneously within it. The previous year, Charles Darwin, together with Alfred Russel Wallace, had published the theory of evolution by natural selection, which provided a mechanism to account for the enormous diversity of species found in nature. Taken alongside Pasteur's work, this theory made the idea of spontaneous generation redundant. In his landmark work, *On the Origin of Species*, published in 1859, Darwin acknowledged that, while life did not arise through spontaneous generation, no coherent explanation existed to replace it, which represented a serious problem for his theory.

In 1924, a significant step forward came in the search for the origins of life, when the Russian biochemist Alexander Oparin proposed that life began in a 'primordial soup'. Oparin suggested that the atmosphere of the early Earth was very different from what it is today, specifically because it lacked oxygen. This reducing atmosphere, as it is known, was composed of methane, ammonia, carbon dioxide and nitrogen, providing suitable conditions for complex organic molecules to be synthesised from simpler inorganic ones already present on Earth, in reactions facilitated by energy from lightning strikes. In 1953, in what would become one of the best-known experiments of the time, Stanley Miller, then a 22-year-old graduate student at the University of Chicago, attempted to

Above: Louis Pasteur, who proved that microorganisms did not arise through spontaneous generation.

recreate the early conditions of the Earth's atmosphere in a laboratory. He introduced the gases then thought to make up the atmosphere, including methane and ammonia, into a sealed flask and subjected these to electric sparks to simulate the action of lightning. This resulted in the synthesis of a number of amino acids, organic compounds which can combine to form proteins, and, as such, can be regarded as the basic building blocks of life. It demonstrated that complex organic substances could be made from simple inorganic ones, providing support for Oparin's primordial soup theory, even if it has not proved possible to produce particular proteins and, ultimately, living cells.

Above: A black smoker in the Pacific Ocean, a type of hydrothermal vent where life may have begun.

TIME AND PLACE

More recent theories on the origin of life generally take Oparin's work as a starting point, even if the idea of a primordial soup is no longer accepted and some of the details of Miller's experiment have been questioned (notably the composition of the gases in his flask, as the mixture he used did not accurately reproduce the composition of the early Earth's atmosphere). It is now thought that, even though the Earth's atmosphere at this time did not contain oxygen, it was either only mildly reducing or neutral, leading to the suggestion that life first began in specific sites where the necessary reducing conditions could be found.

One of the most likely places for life to have begun, receiving the most scientific attention in recent years, is in deep-sea hydrothermal vents. These are underwater geysers found in areas of high seismic activity, and involve water that has seeped into the Earth's crust being heated and forced upwards through cracks until it comes into contact with seawater. Chemicals dissolved in this water are often deposited to form characteristic chimney-like stacks on the ocean floor, and these contain numerous small apertures which, according to some scientists, would make ideal sites for the reactions necessary for life to begin. As well as the required chemicals, a source of energy exists in the vents, in the form of an electrochemical gradient between the acidic water from the vents and the alkaline seawater, which has the potential to fuel reactions synthesising organic compounds. The required energy is generated by the movement of positively charged hydrogen ions, or protons ($H+$), from acidic water (where these ions are in a high concentration) to seawater (where lower concentrations are found). This process has been compared to the energy from a waterfall being harnessed by a turbine, and it works on much the same principle as the source of energy found within all living cells, known as a proton pump.

Even though we cannot say for certain that life began in hydrothermal vents, or in any other specific locations, advances in our understanding of the formation of the Earth have provided us with an approximate date when the event occurred. Life could not have existed before the Hadean eon, the earliest period of the Earth's history, came to an end about 3.9 billion years ago, because intense volcanic activity and numerous asteroid impacts – known as the Late Heavy

Bombardment – during this period produced such adverse conditions on the planet that the emergence of life would not have been possible. By 3.5 billion years ago life definitely existed, because the oldest confirmed examples of fossilised microorganisms were discovered in rocks in Western Australia that date to this time. Traces of what may also be fossils have been found in 3.7-billion-year-old rocks in Greenland, potentially narrowing down the period in which life began, and leading to speculation that it may well have occurred relatively soon after the end of the Late Heavy Bombardment – say about 3.8 billion years ago.

Above: An example of the earliest-known life, a 3.5-billion-year-old stromatolite fossil from Western Australia.

REPLICATING LIFE

The exact details of how simple organic compounds came together to form complex molecules capable of self-replication remain unknown. One theory, known as the 'RNA world', suggests that, before the evolution of cells containing DNA (the long double-stranded molecule which contains the genetic code), the related molecule RNA, which is shorter and single-stranded, existed on its own as a self-replicating molecule, not enclosed by any sort of membrane. According to the theory, this form of RNA would have undergone the process of natural selection as it replicated, leading to the evolution of more complicated molecules and ultimately to DNA. The major problem with this theory is that, in order to replicate, both DNA and RNA require enzymes composed of proteins to catalyse the process, but these enzymes are themselves constructed from codes contained within DNA and RNA. So unless RNA and the necessary proteins evolved together, or RNA somehow catalysed its own replication, it could not have been the first self-replicator. In this case, the first self-replicating molecule was then something entirely different –

Opposite: An illustration of a double-stranded DNA molecule, which contains the genetic code found in all forms of life.

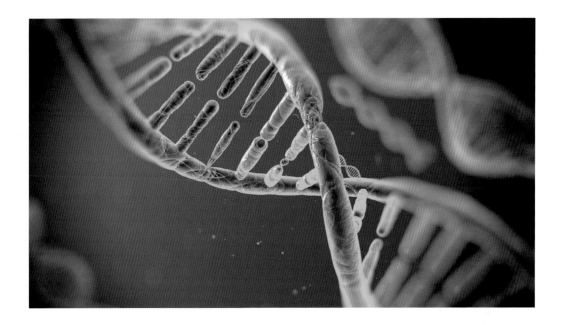

perhaps a precursor to RNA that no longer exists and about which we currently know nothing at all.

Once a self-replicating molecule had emerged, whatever it may have been, natural selection gave rise to the first simple, or prokaryotic, cells, where the reactions involved in replication and metabolism can occur within the protective barrier of the cell wall. Single-celled organisms of this type, bacteria and the later emerging archaea, remained the only forms of life on Earth for a very long period – thought to have been about two billion years – until the emergence of more complex eukaryotic cells. These contain clearly defined organelles, separated from the rest of the cell contents by membranes, in which particular functions of the cell occur. DNA is contained within the nucleus, where the process of replication begins, and energy is produced through respiration in the mitochondria. Plant cells have additional organelles called chloroplasts, which is where photosynthesis occurs. Sugars are synthesised from carbon dioxide, and water and oxygen are released into the

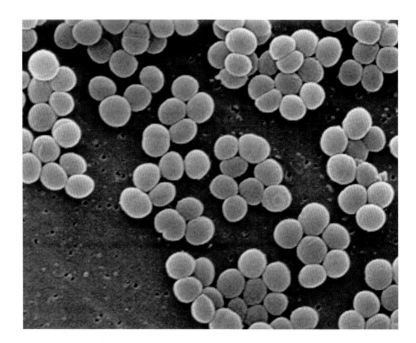

Right: A scanning electron micrograph of *Staphylococcus aureus*, an example of a single-celled bacterium.

atmosphere as a byproduct. In the early evolutionary history of life on Earth, this release of oxygen was of vital importance because it would lead to an accumulation of the gas in the atmosphere, making aerobic respiration possible.

Eukaryotic cells appear to have evolved as a consequence of a symbiotic relationship developing between a number of different types of prokaryotic cell, resulting in some of these cells being absorbed into others and evolving to have the specialised functions now found in the organelles. It has been suggested that this was an extremely rare occurrence in the evolution of life, perhaps only having happened once, but with enormous implications, as we will see in the following pages. This led to the evolution of more complex multicellular forms of life, of which we are just one example.

ALTERNATIVE
THEORIES

We may not know exactly how life began on Earth, but all the various theories put forward start from the obvious position that it began somewhere on the planet. All the theories, that is, except one. The panspermia theory suggests that life did not begin in primordial soups or hydrothermal vents – rather, it first arrived on Earth from outer space. The idea goes back to the late-nineteenth century, which may account for its unusual name, and comes in a variety of forms, most commonly that complex organic molecules arrived on the planet on board asteroids or comets that collided with the Earth, and effectively seeded life on the planet. This idea was not taken very seriously until the 1970s, when it emerged that interstellar dust really does contain complex organic molecules, and that these can be found inside asteroids and comets, where they may be protected from the very high temperatures experienced during entry into the Earth's atmosphere and impact with the ground.

Above: The Earth seen from near space. Did life arrive here from further afield?

The best-known modern proponents of the panspermia theory have been the British astronomer Sir Fred Hoyle and his Sri Lanka-born colleague Chandra Wickramasinghe, who have pointed out that, if correct, it would explain not only how life began but also solve the puzzle of how it got going so quickly. No direct evidence exists to demonstrate that we are all actually aliens, but, then again, no evidence exists to show that life definitely started on Earth either. Perhaps life actually began on Earth before being transported into space to seed other planets.

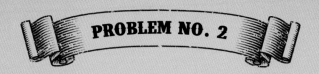
WHAT CAUSED THE CAMBRIAN EXPLOSION?

Field: Geology, palaeontology, taxonomy, evolution
Location: The Burgess Shale in Canada and numerous
other places around the world

Life existed on Earth in simple unicellular forms for about three billion years. Then, all of a sudden and almost out of nowhere, vast numbers of more complex organisms began to appear.

There was a sudden proliferation of multicellular marine life-forms at the beginning of the Cambrian period of geological time. An astonishing variety of animals appeared over the course of about 20 million years, the blink of an eye in a geological time frame, representing almost all of the phyla that exist today, including primitive examples of animals with backbones – chordates, the phylum to which vertebrates such as ourselves belong.

The Cambrian period is usually dated from 542 million years ago to around 485 million years ago. It was first defined and given its name in 1835 by Adam Sedgwick, Professor of Geology at the University of Cambridge, who taught a young Charles Darwin. Sedgwick named the period after the Latin name for Wales, where he had studied Cambrian rock formations and where he regularly led geology field trips – one of which was attended by Darwin shortly before he set off aboard HMS *Beagle* on the worldwide voyage that would make his name as a naturalist.

DARWIN'S DILEMMA

Darwin's study of geology played an important role while he developed his theory of evolution by natural selection, particularly affecting his awareness of the gradual changes that occur in geological formations over long periods of time. In *On the Origin of Species*, Darwin envisaged natural selection working in a similar way, gradually and over a long period of time. He describes how an isolated population of one species could be transformed into a separate species by small incremental stages, due to the accumulation of relatively minor variations. In one part of the book, he provided answers to the many criticisms he knew his theory would face once published, but struggled to find an answer to the appearance of such a wide diversity of life during the early part of the Cambrian period. He wrote, 'There is another and allied difficulty, which is much graver. I allude to the manner in which numbers of species of the same group, suddenly appear in the lowest known fossiliferous rocks.'

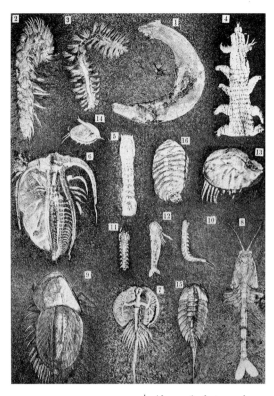

Above: A photograph of Middle-Cambrian fossils collected from the Burgess Shale in Canada, showing the considerable variation in specimens dating from this period.

Darwin attempted to explain the appearance of so many life-forms in what would become known as the Cambrian explosion by suggesting that any organisms existing before this period had simply not survived in the fossil record. What he did not attempt to do was offer an explanation for the sudden proliferation of such a wide variety of life, beyond recognising that this unexplained phenomenon presented a serious challenge to his theory. This has become known as Darwin's dilemma and, while no longer considered to present a challenge to evolutionary theory, which is backed up by a huge body of evidence, it has not been entirely resolved today.

THE BURGESS SHALE

Fossils from Cambrian rocks were well-known in Darwin's day. These included numerous examples of trilobites, marine arthropods that resemble very large woodlice (the largest-known trilobite fossil is 70 cm (27.5 inches) long). As with many Cambrian fauna, trilobites appear in the fossil record fully formed from about 540 million years ago, with no trace of any ancestral or transitional species ever being found. Like many of the other examples of Cambrian fossils found in the nineteenth century, trilobites were hard-bodied, having a tough exoskeleton which, in most cases, was the body part to become fossilised.

Few soft-bodied animals were known from this period until after 1909, when Charles Doolittle Walcott discovered an extensive fossil field known as the Burgess Shale in the Canadian Rockies

Opposite: Charles Doolittle Walcott (left), working in the Burgess Shale fossil quarry with his son and daughter.

Left: A typical example of a trilobite fossil from the Cambrian period.

of British Columbia. Walcott had been the director of the United States Geological Survey and was at the time of the discovery the secretary of the Smithsonian Institute in Washington. He spent most of his remaining career working on the fossils from the Burgess Shale. There were not only vast numbers of fossils in the shale (Walcott collected about 65,000), but many were exceptionally well preserved and included soft body parts of animals, as well as exoskeletons and bones. His work transformed our understanding of the Cambrian fauna, previously thought to have been dominated by hard-bodied animals – in fact, these only made up slightly more than ten per cent of the total fauna.

The shale is a sedimentary mudstone, formed about 509 million years ago as a result of mudslides onto the ocean floor, which was then raised upwards by seismic activity. The reasons soft-bodied animals, which usually decay before fossilisation can occur, were so well preserved are not fully understood, but over the years an astonishing variety of often bizarre-looking creatures has been found. One of the strangest was named *Hallucigenia*, a small arthropod with eight pairs of legs and numerous spines on its back. *Pikaia* does not look so strange, bearing a resemblance to a flattened eel, but it too has received a great deal of attention, because it is the oldest-known chordate.

LIFE EVOLVING

The remarkable finds in the Burgess Shale were well-known among palaeontologists, but came to the attention of a much wider audience after 1989, when the American evolutionary biologist and writer Stephen Jay Gould published *Wonderful Life: The Burgess Shale and the Nature of History*. Gould, along with his colleague Niles Eldredge, had previously developed the theory of the punctuated equilibrium, in which he envisaged evolution occurring in short rapid bursts that interrupted long periods of relative stability, rather than being a gradual and continuous process, as Darwin had thought it to be. The theory did not meet with universal agreement among other evolutionary biologists – and was vociferously opposed by Richard Dawkins – but it could at least account for the variety of life that appeared during the Cambrian explosion.

Various theories have attempted to explain the explosion, suggesting that a rise in oxygen levels in the atmosphere, known to have occurred at about the same time, allowed animals with more complicated metabolisms to arise. Or that the evolution of the eye, first observed at the beginning of the Cambrian period, led to an increase in predation and a subsequent arms race between predators and prey. Environmental and climatic changes leading up to the Cambrian period could have caused a mass extinction event among those multicellular organisms predating the period, known as the Ediacaran biota, expanding the range of ecological niches for animals to fill. But whatever the case, and despite the fact that much of the Cambrian fauna would itself later become extinct, the explosion was the beginning of much greater complexity and diversity of life on Earth.

— ALTERNATIVE —
THEORIES

Left: An illustration of what today's Earth might look like if it underwent a rotation of 90 degrees during a major incidence of true polar wander.

In 1997 Joe Kirschvink, a geobiologist at the California Institute of Technology in Pasadena, proposed that the Cambrian explosion was partly caused by a massive and rapid incidence of true polar wander. This is a geophysical phenomenon that occurs because the Earth is not a perfect sphere, so does not spin exactly on its axis – rather wobbling, or wandering, as it turns. The uneven spread of continents around the equator is thought to accentuate this effect. The extent of true polar wander is usually measured in fractions of a degree, but Kirschvink suggested that, during a period coinciding with the Cambrian explosion, the Earth underwent a rotation of 90 degrees, meaning that land that had been at the poles was shifted to the equator. This would have occurred over the course of about 15 million years – an incredibly short period compared to the hundreds of millions of years such movement would take as the result of plate tectonics. According to the theory, one of the many consequences of this massive wander was an enormous release of methane from the polar regions, causing the climate to warm dramatically and creating the sort of conditions which would favour a rapid burst of evolution. Kirschvink has described this as being the methane fuse that ignited the Cambrian explosion and, though initially greeted with a great deal of scepticism, enough geological evidence has since been found to suggest that the idea may not be as crazy as it sounds.

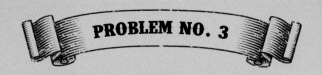

WHY DID THE DINOSAURS DIE OUT?

Field: Geology, palaeontology
Location: Around the world

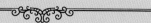

According to the fossil record, dinosaurs were Earth's dominant land animals for more than 100 million years before becoming almost entirely extinct in a relatively short space of time.

Many terrestrial and marine organisms died out around 66 million years ago in what is known as the Cretaceous–Tertiary (K–T) extinction event. Over the years, a variety of theories have been put forward to explain this sudden disappearance – many suggesting that it was a consequence of a catastrophic event. But, even though scientific research over the course of the last few decades has provided us with a good idea of what may have happened, we do not yet know for certain.

The dividing line between the Cretaceous period and the Tertiary (the early part of which is now often called the Palaeogene) can be seen around the world in rock formations that have not been through subsequent geological activity or erosion. The so-called K–T boundary takes the form of a thin grey band of clay, separating layers of sometimes very different sedimentary rocks. The range of fossils found below this grey line is distinctive of the Cretaceous period, comprising dinosaurs and a wide range of animals which became extinct at the same time, including a number of large marine reptiles such as the enormous plesiosaurs, and the ammonites (molluscs with spiral shells, which are among the most common fossils found today). Above the line, there is an increasing number of mammals and birds that evolved from the species that survived the extinction event, and diversified to occupy the ecological niches newly made available.

THE IMPACT EVENT

In 1980 a team of scientists – led by the American Nobel Prize-winning physicist Luis Alvarez and his son, the geologist Walter Alvarez – published research which indicated that the K–T boundary was caused by a large meteorite hitting the Earth 66 million years ago. They concluded that a consequence of this impact was the extinction event. Their primary evidence was their discovery of very high levels of the metal iridium in the K–T

Below: The exposed K–T boundary in Alberta, Canada. A thin band of clay separates two different types of rock.

boundary clay – hundreds of times higher than in the Earth's crust, where it is extremely rare. Iridium is relatively abundant in comets and asteroids, leading the team to speculate that the colossal explosion caused by a large impact event would have vaporised the meteorite, and the resulting dust would have blown into the upper atmosphere, spreading around the world, along with huge amounts of other debris. The amount of dust in the atmosphere would have dramatically changed the climate for years to come by blocking sunlight from reaching the Earth's surface. This would have caused a rapid cooling of temperatures and reduced the ability of plants to photosynthesise, leading to conditions that would have been particularly difficult for large animals to survive – proving catastrophic for the dinosaurs and for much of the rest of life on Earth, and causing the extinction of an estimated 75 per cent of all animals and plants.

THE CHICXULUB CRATER

The theory that the K–T extinction had been caused by a meteorite was not new at the time of the discovery of iridium in the boundary clay, but this provided the first direct evidence that a huge impact had taken place. What Luis and Walter Alvarez did not know was the location of the impact, which, it would later emerge, had actually already been discovered a few years before they published their theory, during an oil company's geological exploration of the Yucatán Peninsula in Mexico. Details of the find finally emerged in the 1990s and were confirmed as the site

Opposite: A magnified grain of shocked quartz from K–T boundary clay, indicating a meteorite impact.

Below: The location of the Chicxulub impact, off the coast of the Yucatán Peninsula in Mexico.

of the impact by analysis of rock samples taken from the area. These contained shocked quartz, a mineral formed when quartz in the Earth's crust is subjected to the sort of immense pressure that can only occur naturally when a meteorite hits the planet. Rocks from the sample proved to be 66 million years old, and geological mapping of Yucatán uncovered what remains of the crater, which is 300 km (190 miles) wide and was caused by a meteorite estimated to have been about 16 km (10 miles) in diameter. The centre of the crater, where the meteorite hit, is just off the coast of the Yucatán Peninsula, near the town of Chicxulub, and further evidence of the impact has been found in the form of layers of debris left by the huge tsunami it caused, which can be seen in numerous places around the Gulf of Mexico and the Caribbean. The approximate match in the dating for the K–T extinction and the Chicxulub meteorite impact, together with the presence

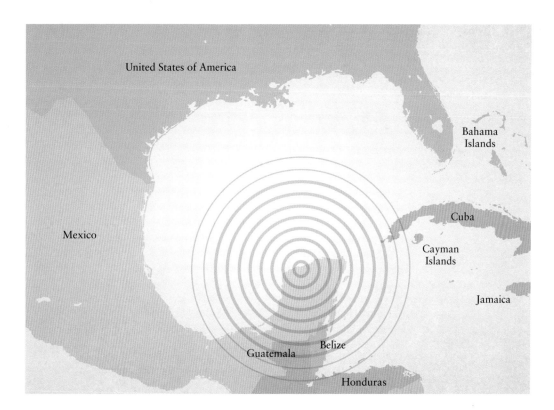

United States of America

Bahama Islands

Cuba

Mexico

Cayman Islands

Jamaica

Belize

Guatemala

Honduras

of dinosaur fossils below the K–T boundary but not above it, certainly provide good lines of circumstantial evidence that the two are linked – but this does not amount to definitive proof. Some palaeontologists still dispute the link, pointing out that the datings would have to match exactly, or suggesting that the meteorite strike was one factor among a number that came together to cause the extinction. One scenario, for instance, envisages the dinosaurs coming under pressure from more gradual climate change, in which the warm conditions of the Cretaceous period were coming to an end and the colder climate of the Tertiary was beginning. The sudden changes to the climate brought on by the Chicxulub meteorite could then have been the final straw, finishing off the dinosaurs and those other species adapted to a warmer climate, and in the process, opening up the way for the rise of mammals.

FEATHERED DINOSAURS

In a sense the dinosaurs did not become totally extinct 66 million years ago, but remain with us in the form of birds, which are now widely accepted as having evolved from theropod dinosaurs, a group including the fearsome *Tyrannosaurus rex*. The idea of a link between the two began in the 1860s, when it was proposed by Thomas Henry Huxley, a friend and vociferous supporter of Charles Darwin. The discovery of the fossilised skeleton of the feathered dinosaur *Archaeopteryx* in a quarry in southern Germany in 1861, now housed in London's Natural History Museum, provided some evidence for the theory, but it would not become widely accepted until the 1990s, when fossils of a number of other species of feathered dinosaurs were found in the Liaoning province of northeast China. Subsequent research in comparative anatomy – and what we can gather about the behaviour of certain dinosaurs – has backed up findings of a close link between the two. So you can now state when watching the blackbirds in your garden that their ancestors survived the K–T extinction event, and they could be regarded as living, if distant, relatives of *T. rex*.

— ALTERNATIVE —
THEORIES

Above: Layers of flood basalt exposed by erosion in the Deccan Traps near Pune in western India.

The Chicxulub meteor strike was not the only major catastrophe to occur at about the time of the K–T extinction event. Enormous volcanic eruptions in the western region of central India are also thought to have begun about 66 million years ago and then continued for tens of thousands of years, forming a vast lava field, the remains of which can be seen today in the multiple layers of basalt rock known as the Deccan Traps. One theory suggests that the eruptions were the result of a plume of molten rock rising from the Earth's core through the mantle to form magma when it reached the crust, which then flowed out onto the Earth's surface. The resulting basalt flood is thought to have covered almost half the area of modern India, much of which has since eroded, and this would have been accompanied by the emission of sulphur dioxide into the atmosphere on such a vast scale that it must have had a dramatic impact on the climate.

Before details of the Chicxulub meteor strike were known, it had been argued by some palaeontologists that the Deccan Traps eruptions on their own could have been responsible for the extinction of the dinosaurs and those other animals which died out at the same time. This theory is not now as widely accepted as the meteorite impact theory, but it could nevertheless be the case that the climatic disruption caused by the eruptions played some part in the K–T extinctions, perhaps forming a deadly combination with the meteor strike that sealed the fate of the dinosaurs.

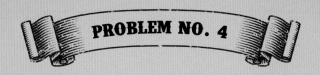

HOW DO MIGRATING ANIMALS FIND THEIR WAY?

Field: Zoology, ethology
Location: In the case of Arctic terns, literally around the world

The ability shown by some animals to find their way when migrating over long distances intrigues and amazes us. The puzzle of how they do this is difficult to solve and we are only really just beginning to find answers.

Some of the migratory habits of animals are truly astonishing, not least because without our own navigational aids, our compasses and our GPS systems, we very easily get lost ourselves. Arctic terns leave their northern breeding grounds in and around the Arctic Circle towards the end of summer to fly south all the way to the Antarctic coast, arriving in time for the onset of the summer in the southern hemisphere, and then fly all the way back to the Arctic to breed the following spring. If the terns flew directly between their two destinations, this would involve journeys totaling over 32,000 km (20,000 miles), but they actually adopt much more convoluted routes, increasing the distances they cover by tens of thousands of miles. Yet after covering such enormous distances, the terns often return to the exact spot where they bred the previous year.

Atlantic salmon spend most of their adult lives in the ocean before returning to the same river where they were born, and usually to the same stretch of that river, to spawn. Some monarch butterflies are involved in a circular migration – which takes several generations to complete, travelling from southern Canada to overwintering sites in central Mexico – while every year, millions of Christmas Island crabs travel from the forest in the interior of their Indian Ocean island to the coast to breed. Several species of frogs and toads engage in similar annual mass migrations, and sea turtles such as loggerheads and leatherbacks give the impression of being engaged in a lifelong migration, swimming for what can be thousands of kilometres between breeding grounds on beaches and feeding grounds in the distant ocean.

Above: Every autumn millions of butterflies return to the Monarch Butterfly Biosphere Reserve in Michoacán, Mexico.

NAVIGATING ANIMALS

These birds, fish, butterflies, crabs and turtles provide a few examples from among the thousands of species of animals that engage in migratory behaviour of one sort or another. Charles Darwin thought that animals, and to some extent humans as well, possessed an instinctive ability to orientate themselves in their surroundings, which they could use to navigate by dead reckoning, but he could not be any more specific about how this ability worked. Beginning in the 1910s, the Austrian animal behaviourist Karl von Frisch carried out experimental research on honeybees, which showed that their primary means of navigation involved using the position of the Sun to orientate themselves, but that they could also detect and follow the pattern of ultraviolet light in blue skies, which is caused by polarisation and is invisible to human eyes. On cloudy days, Frisch found that the bees could also make use of the Earth's magnetic field to find their way when the Sun and polarised light were not visible. He would also be the first to describe the so-called waggle dance that the bees engaged in as a means of communicating the location of a source of nectar they had found to other bees in a hive.

Since Frisch's work, which earned him a Nobel Prize in 1973, other animals, such as sea turtles, have also been found to be able to detect the Earth's magnetic field. Homing pigeons, which can return to their own lofts after being released hundreds of kilometres away, appear to use the magnetic field as one of a range of navigation techniques. Attempts have been made to discover how pigeons detect the magnetic field, which is actually very weak, and while we do not know for certain, one theory suggests they somehow make use of particles of magnetite, a highly magnetic mineral of iron oxide found in the upper part of their beaks. Even so, it remains a mystery how the navigational information that may be gained in this way is passed to the brain and processed.

Homing pigeons can switch between different methods of navigation as circumstances dictate, sometimes following known landmarks, such as coastlines, rivers and roads, while at others navigating by the Sun and stars. When it is too dark or cloudy for them to see the sky, they can fall back on finding their way by following the magnetic field. Researchers at the University of

— ALTERNATIVE — THEORIES

Above: The robin's ability to navigate using the Earth's magnetic field may be due to a quantum phenomenon.

Research into the ability of European robins to use the Earth's magnetic field to navigate suggests that the mechanism involved may work at a subatomic, or quantum, level. If this proves to be the case, then it would go some way to explaining how animals can detect and make use of the natural magnetic field, which is far too weak to provide enough energy to power any molecular chemical reactions. Magnetoreception, as this ability is known, appears to function through the eyes of the robin, so it is possible that light provides the energy required to activate so-called radical pairs, subatomic charged particles that are small enough to be influenced by the low levels of magnetism and may create some form of navigational signal that is then passed to the robin's brain via the optic nerve.

Texas who monitored the brain activity of pigeons while they were subjected to a moving magnetic field came to the conclusion that, as well as having compasses inside their heads, the pigeons somehow constructed maps in their brains as they went along, so when they ended up in a place they had never been before they could head straight for home. We may like to think of ourselves as rather more intelligent than pigeons, but, for all our superior brainpower, we can't do that.

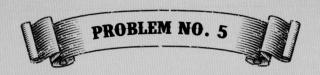

WHAT IS AT THE BOTTOM OF THE SEA?

Field: Oceanography, marine biology, exploration
Location: The deep ocean

Beyond the shallow waters of the continental shelves surrounding landmasses lies the deep ocean, one of the least-explored and least-known regions on the surface of the Earth.

A t a time when we are capable of landing a spacecraft on a comet, as the *Rosetta* mission did in November 2014, investigating the bottom of the sea still presents us with formidable challenges. Since 1872, when the *Challenger* Expedition set out on the first serious scientific study of the deep ocean, it is estimated that we have only discovered about five per cent of the animals and plants which live in this habitat, and almost all of the ocean floor is only known to us through low-resolution maps made by echo-sounding from the surface.

Until the middle of the nineteenth century, the prevailing view was that the deep ocean was a barren and lifeless void. Given the harsh conditions encountered at even a relatively modest depth, it was a reasonable conclusion to reach. Pressure increases quickly with depth, by one atmosphere for every 10 metres (33 ft), and sunlight hardly penetrates beyond 200 metres (660 ft), so after this point no photosynthesis can occur. It is pitch black and very cold, and the salt water and high pressure lead to temperatures well below freezing – all conditions extremely hostile for burgeoning life.

THE *CHALLENGER* EXPEDITION

By the 1860s, in part as a consequence of the publication of Charles Darwin's theory of evolution by natural selection, attempts had begun to investigate the deep ocean. The Scottish natural historian Charles Wyville Thomson witnessed one such attempt in Norway, where life-forms were found in a dredge taken from a deep fjord, prompting him to propose an expedition to the Royal Society in London, aimed at exploring the deep ocean. The Royal Society secured the cooperation of the Royal Navy, who provided a ship, HMS *Challenger*, and crew. This gives an indication of the influence the society commanded at that time, and of the navy's commitment to mounting voyages of exploration – even if, on this

Below: An Illustration of HMS *Challenger* from the final report of the expedition, published in 1895.

occasion, they were perhaps a little more motivated by the need to improve their new practice of laying underwater telegraph cables.

The *Challenger* set out from Britain in December 1872, having had its guns removed and scientific laboratories installed. It was the first time a voyage had been undertaken principally for scientific purposes. Prior to this, navy expeditions were mainly for surveying and charting, with a view to future colonisation or commercial exploitation. The *Beagle*, for instance, is now remembered because of Charles Darwin's visit to the Galápagos Islands, but at the time the intention was to chart the coast of South America, to give Britain a strategic advantage over its European rivals.

During the *Challenger*'s proposed circumnavigation of the globe, the scientists on board, led by Wyville Thomson, planned to investigate the physical and chemical properties of the deep ocean, and collect samples of ocean floor sediments and marine life by dredging the seabed and trawling in deep water. The voyage lasted three and a half years, covered 128,000 km (69,000 nautical miles) and, once it had returned to Britain, the report on its findings took 20 years to compile and consisted of 50 large volumes.

THE BIRTH OF OCEANOGRAPHY

The expedition resulted in enormous advances in our understanding of the oceans, and thousands of species new to science were classified. It is now considered to have marked the beginning of the science of oceanography and, more widely, it bridged the gap between the way science had been conducted previously, led by what may be described as gentlemen amateurs, such as Darwin, and being the province of professional specialists attached to a university or another institution. What it did not do was produce any groundbreaking discoveries attracting public attention, as previous voyages had done. Moreover, at least according to John Murray, one of the principal scientists involved, it had failed in its ultimate intention. This had been to test

Darwin's theory that life had first evolved in the oceans and that the deep seas contained a repository of ancient life-forms that had become extinct in shallower waters. Actually it was found that, while the deep seas and ocean floors were teeming with life, none of what had been discovered provided any missing links in the evolutionary tree of life. As we have seen in 'How did life on Earth begin?' (page 10), it would be more than a hundred years later that oceanographers first proposed that life itself began in and around deep-sea hydrothermal vents.

PHANTOMS FROM THE DEEP

The *Challenger* Expedition established that life exists throughout the oceans, even in the deepest parts and on the sea floor. The difficulties and expense involved in studying this region mean that, despite more than 140 years of research, little, if anything, is known about most deep-sea organisms. The colossal squid, for instance, is thought to be the largest invertebrate on Earth, yet it is known only through two samples brought up by deep-sea fishermen, despite being relatively common in deep water – a fact inferred from the recovery of the squids' indigestible beaks in the stomachs of whales.

It has become clear that organisms have evolved a variety of ways to exist in the extreme conditions found in the deep ocean. Many have very slow metabolic rates as a means of dealing with the cold and lack of food, often living on whatever organic matter sinks

Below: An illustration from the *Challenger* report of the variations of the protozoa *Radiolaria* collected during the expedition.

The Voyage of H.M.S. "Challenger."   Radiolaria Pl. 113.

CASTANELLA.

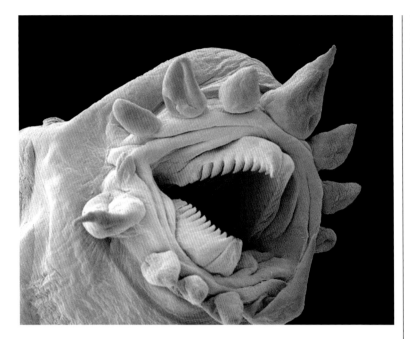

Left: Scanning electron micrograph of the mouth parts of the deep-ocean scale worm *Lepidonotopodium piscesae*.

from the more productive zones above. Invertebrates have jelly-like bodies, where the pressure within is the same as in the ocean, so they are not crushed, while fish often have very large eyes to see in the low levels of light, and huge jaws providing them with the best chance of catching scarce prey, often giving them an otherworldly appearance when they are brought up to the surface.

A number of organisms, such as the aptly named lanternfish, one of the most common deep-sea fish, exhibit bioluminescence, the ability to produce and emit light. Some organisms can live in the superheated water of hydrothermal vents, where temperatures can exceed 298°C (570°F), while *Osedax*, or boneworms, live on the bones of dead whales that have sunk to the ocean floor. Boneworms have no mouth or stomach, instead using root-like outgrowths to penetrate bones and extract nutrients. These and the thousands of other species we have found in deep water are, to coin a phrase, a drop in the ocean compared to the thousands, if not millions, of organisms we currently know nothing about.

ALTERNATIVE THEORIES

Above: The bathyscaphe *Trieste*, in which Walsh and Piccard descended to the bottom of the Challenger Deep.

The scientists on the *Challenger* Expedition had to make do with sampling techniques that could be employed at the surface, for instance, taking soundings using a weighted plumb line. The darkness and extreme high pressure prevented them from observing anything below the uppermost layer of water. The first submersibles began to be used in the 1930s and, in 1960, a US Navy mission carrying Don Walsh and Jacques Piccard descended to the bottom of the Challenger Deep, a depression in the floor of the Mariana Trench which, at almost 11,000 metres (over 36,000 ft), is the deepest known point in the oceans. The trench is located near the Mariana Islands in the Pacific Ocean, to the east of the Philippines, and was first sounded in 1875 by members of the *Challenger* Expedition. A number of remotely operated vehicles (ROVs) have since been used to explore the Challenger Deep, but it would be 2012 before a third person – the film director James Cameron – made a descent, giving an indication of the difficulties of operating at such extreme depths, where the pressure is more than a thousand times greater than at the surface. Even so, life has been observed at the bottom of the Challenger Deep, mostly in the form of various types of soft-bodied invertebrates. After his 1960 descent, Jacques Piccard reported glimpsing some type of flat fish. If he was right, it would be truly remarkable for a fish with a bony skeleton to survive at such depths – but, then again, evolution has sprung surprises on us before.

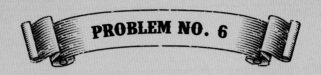
HOW DO OUR GENES MAKE US HUMAN?

Field: Genetics, molecular biology, epigenetics
Location: In our DNA

One thing common to all life on Earth, from bacteria to blue whales to bonobos, is a genetic code contained within strands of DNA. This leads to the perplexing question of how our DNA creates human beings.

Long sections of genetic code are identical across the entire span of life. About 50 per cent of our own DNA sequence is the same as bananas', while we share 98 per cent of our DNA with chimpanzees. So what makes us different?

In April 2003, a major milestone in the study of human genetics was reached with the publication of the complete human genome. An enormous collaborative project, worked on by scientists in 20 different countries, it may well come to be regarded in the same light as the great scientific landmarks. Principal among these was the work of the Augustinian monk Gregor Mendel – often referred to as the 'father of genetics' – which he carried out in the 1850s and '60s and which first established the rules of heredity, as well as James Watson and Francis Crick's 1953 description of the molecular structure of DNA as the now-famous double helix.

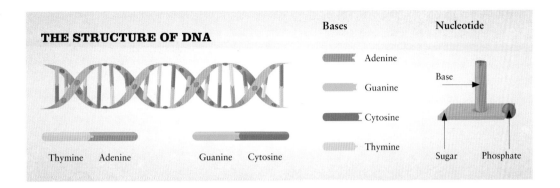

THE STRUCTURE OF DNA

Thymine   Adenine   Guanine   Cytosine

Bases

Adenine

Guanine

Cytosine

Thymine

Nucleotide

Base

Sugar   Phosphate

Above: A diagram showing the structure of DNA and the base pairs that carry genetic code.

GENE EXPRESSION

The published genome contains the sequence of some three billion so-called base pairs, which constitute the genetic code in our DNA. The translation of the code made up by these base pairs is used to build up 20 different essential amino acids which, together with other amino acids we get from our food, combine in numerous different ways to form all the different proteins we require in our bodies. Geneticists used to think that the role of DNA was almost entirely concerned with providing a template for the manufacture of these proteins, but the complete genome showed that the sections of DNA which perform this function, our genes, only account for about two per cent of the total.

The function of the remaining 98 per cent, sometimes known as 'junk DNA', is not entirely known, but it has become increasingly apparent that much of it is not junk at all. It plays a role in, among other things, gene expression. This is the actual process by which the information contained in our genes is used to make up all the different tissues and organs in our body, through the process known as cell differentiation. Here, stem cells divide to produce different types of cells, such as liver cells or nerve cells. Unravelling the way in which one type of cell divides to produce a wide variety of different cells has proved to be extremely difficult and is currently one of the principal areas of genetic research.

The basic functioning of DNA in producing amino acids from the genetic code is relatively straightforward: the double-stranded DNA molecule effectively unzips, splitting apart the base pairs and revealing the code that is then copied by single-stranded RNA and used to assemble amino acids. But the control of this process, in which the required genes are activated and those not needed switched off, appears to be extremely complicated. Each advance in our knowledge of gene expression uncovers a whole new level of complexity that has to be unravelled. Beyond that, there is also the equally tricky problem of determining how, during the process of protein folding, the proteins made from genes assume the particular three-dimensional shape that determines their functions. The potential applications of our advancing knowledge of gene expression and protein folding are wide, not least in increasing our understanding and ability to treat diseases which have a genetic basis, prominent among which are many forms of cancer.

THE DIFFICULTIES OF CLONING

Another landmark in genetic research was achieved in 1996, when the first mammal (known as Dolly the Sheep) was cloned by geneticists at the University of Edinburgh in Scotland, using a technique called somatic cell nuclear transfer. This involves the removal of a nucleus containing genetic material from a cell of the animal to be cloned, and its introduction into an egg from which the original nucleus has been removed. The egg is then implanted into a surrogate mother and, in theory at least, will develop into an embryo with DNA identical to the animal from which the nucleus was taken.

Needless to say, if it were as easy as that, cloning would be a common occurrence today. In reality, it has proved much more difficult, in part because of the complications which arise as a consequence of gene expression. In some successful cloning experiments, for instance, the observable traits, or phenotype as it is known, of the cloned offspring are not always the same as those

ALTERNATIVE
THEORIES

In recent years, it has become increasingly apparent that gene expression is not controlled solely by DNA, but is also influenced by a number of external factors collectively known as epigenetics. This is a very new field of research and the details of how it works are disputed, but, in essence, it implies that the environment in which DNA replication occurs during cell division can influence the activity of genes and, in doing so, can have an effect on the resulting phenotype. This is thought to occur at a molecular level, through environmental factors modifying the actions of those proteins that surround strands of DNA and influencing the switching off or activation of genes. These epigenetic modifications do not change the DNA sequence of base

Above: Laboratory research on epigenetics investigates the influence of environmental factors on gene expression.

pairs, so are not inherited by future generations, even if those generations may then be subjected to the same environmental conditions as the parent, resulting in similar epigenetic modifications.

of the original animal. So, despite being genetically identical, the offspring looks different from the parent. In order to reproduce exact copies of the original, the process of cloning has to solve the complicated issues involved with gene expression, including the role of junk DNA in regulating genes. We are, it appears, a long way from seeing flocks of cloned sheep.

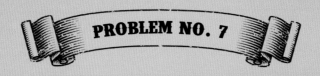

HOW CAN WE DEAL WITH GLOBAL POPULATION GROWTH?

Field: Demography, statistical analysis, agronomy, medicine
Location: Worldwide

With population numbers projected to continue to swell over the course of the twenty-first century, there are some pressing questions that remain unresolved. We turn to science in search of solutions to Earth's depleting space and resources.

The subject of global population growth can be an emotive one, and many accounts of rising populations are accompanied by dire warnings of impending catastrophe. Concern about population growth is by no means a modern phenomenon, though. In 1798, the British cleric Thomas Malthus published *An Essay on the Principle of Population*, in which he addressed the potential problems that could develop due to the rapidly rising population in Britain at that time, a consequence of the Industrial Revolution. He argued that populations had the capacity to grow more quickly than food production, writing, 'The power of population is so superior to the power of the earth to produce subsistence for man, that premature death must in some shape or other visit the human race.' It would become a highly influential concept and one that would reach beyond demography alone – acknowledged, for instance, by Charles Darwin as having been one of the key ideas that led to his theory of evolution by natural selection, which described competition for resources as being one of the driving forces behind evolution.

THE POPULATION BOMB

In 1968, the American entomologist and environmentalist Paul Ehrlich wrote in Malthusian terms in *The Population Bomb* of an upcoming catastrophe, in which many millions of people would die of starvation. Though not the first book to examine the so-called 'population problem', its popularity introduced the issue to a much wider audience. It was followed in 1972 by the even more widely read *The Limits to Growth*, a collaborative report commissioned by the political think tank the Club of Rome. Both works were relatively sober, informed assessments, but were followed by a range of sensationalist books and articles, containing various prophecies of doom – which remain a feature of environmental discussions today.

In *The Population Bomb*, Ehrlich wrote that the Earth could support two billion people before disaster ensued – a figure that had already been exceeded by more than a billion at the time the book was published. Now, almost 50 years later, the predicted catastrophic collapse has not occurred (at least not yet anyway). In July 2015, the Population Division of the United Nations Department of Economics and Social Affairs in New York released the annual revision to its 2010 population census, providing estimates of the global population over the course of this century. According to this, the global population was 7.3 billion in 2015, and was expected to continue growing, reaching 10 billion

Below: Paul Ehrlich, whose book brought the population problem to the attention of a much wider audience.

by the middle of the century and 11.2 billion by 2100, by which time the rate of growth is expected to have slowed – before stabilising and perhaps beginning to fall.

By no means do all demographers agree with the UN figures. The wide variation between experts' population predictions is a consequence of the number of unknown factors involved, and because in reality people rarely behave exactly as expected. But, if we take the UN figures as a reasonable estimate, over the next three to four decades an additional 3 billion people will inhabit the world, and the total figure will be five times higher than Paul Ehrlich's estimated carrying capacity of the Earth.

THE IMPACT OF SCIENCE

One of the ways science has helped to avert potential disasters is through agricultural research aimed at increasing food produce. One of the best-known examples of this is the Green Revolution on the Indian subcontinent, which began in the 1960s – a period

Opposite: A typically crowded scene at a street market in Mumbai, India.

when India and Pakistan were experiencing population booms that appeared to be outstripping the capacity of the region's agriculture to produce enough food for everyone. New varieties of high-yielding wheat, developed by the American agronomist Norman Borlaug at a research station in Mexico, were transferred to the subcontinent, greatly increasing agricultural productivity and averting the potential for widespread famine.

Subsequent research produced new varieties of other staple crops, including rice, and these, together with the use of new technologies in the shape of farm machinery, fertilisers and pesticides, have had a dramatic impact on the amount of food produced – even if these technical advancements can come with social and environmental costs. It has become clear that new technology on its own is not a complete solution, though, and extreme poverty can lead to people remaining malnourished despite there being no local food shortages, through not having land to grow crops themselves or the means to buy enough food.

Below: Wheat harvesting on a family farm in India, where 50 per cent of the population work in agriculture.

Science can also help in the field of healthcare, through the development of medical technology and drugs that address the particular problems causing high levels of child mortality, which are often encountered in those parts of the world where high rates of population growth occur. When such technologies are combined with more widely available healthcare services, the resulting reduction in child mortality often leads to lower rates of population growth. Put simply, women have fewer children in places where those children are more likely to survive into adulthood, and so population numbers gradually begin to stabilise.

HOPE FOR THE FUTURE

The UN figures show that growth rates have already slowed down in many parts of the world. Europe, North and South America and Oceania now show no growth at all, and nor does much of Asia, with the notable exceptions of India and Pakistan. About three-quarters of the population growth set to occur over the course of this century is projected to be on the African continent, and this rise will almost all be as a consequence of people living longer, rather than an increase in the number of children being born. This statistic is key to gaining an understanding of how population growth should slow down and eventually stabilise in the future; improvements in healthcare initially lead to a rapid rise in life expectancy, so, rather than a rising population being caused by more children being born, it is actually a consequence of there being an increased number of older people. Over time, the initial rapid increase in life expectancy will tend to level off and, at this point, the population will stop rising as well.

In the future, then, there will be many more people in the world, and it does appear that population growth is set to continue in the long term. The challenges ahead are to grow enough food, to alleviate extreme poverty and to provide adequate healthcare for the entire global population.

ALTERNATIVE THEORIES

Above: Hans Rosling in the middle of making a point during one of his lectures on global population growth.

Unlike the doom merchants who have until recently dominated the public debate on population growth, the Swedish doctor and statistician Hans Rosling describes himself as a possibilist, believing not only that the Earth can support 11 billion people, but that all of them can enjoy a good quality of life. He appears to be on a mission to make population statistics entertaining as well as informative, making use of dynamic graphics to illustrate his lectures and enlivening proceedings with plenty of jokes, mostly at his own expense.

To take just one example from many, Rosling describes the washing machine as being one of the great inventions of the twentieth century because of the impact it has had on freeing women from domestic drudgery, allowing them the time to do other things, like going to university and getting a job. As he points out, the statistics show that as women become better educated, they gain more control over their lives – over the age at which they start a family and the number of children they have. Where they have the choice, many women opt to have children later in life than their mothers and grandmothers did, and often prefer to have two or three children rather than five or six. This phenomenon has been seen around the world and has often occurred over the course of a single generation. Rosling is not trying to say that this is entirely caused by the washing machine, rather using it to illustrate the point that the empowerment of women has been one of the driving forces behind the observed reduction in population growth rates.

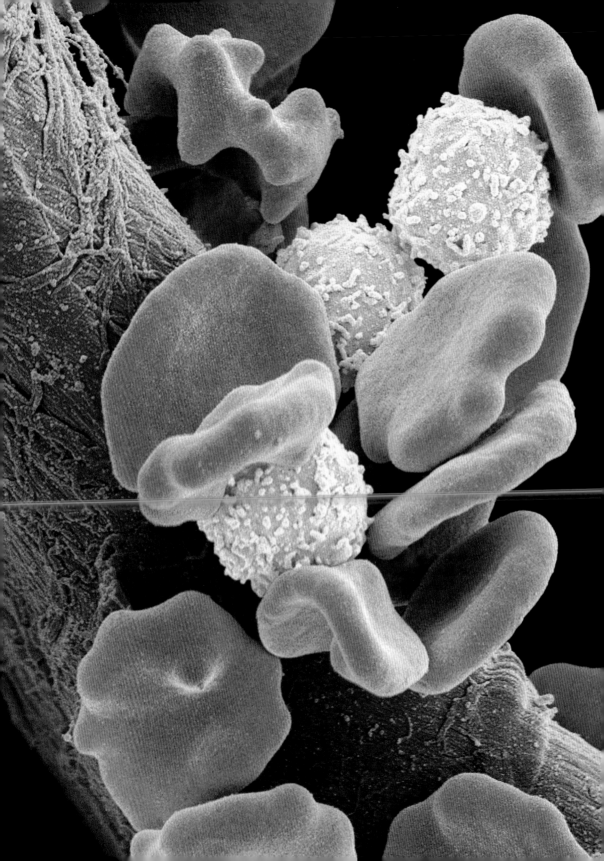

MEDICINE AND NEUROSCIENCE

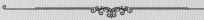

The rise of modern medicine over the course of the past few centuries has been one of the great triumphs of human endeavour. We are now capable of preventing and treating a wide range of diseases once responsible for the deaths of millions of people. Of the many challenges that remain, we look at attempts to find a cure for cancer and a vaccine for HIV, and consider how the misuse of antibiotics can increase bacterial resistance. We then look at the possibility that scientific advances could eventually create eternal life. As life expectancy and knowledge of the process of ageing have expanded, the potential to increase our life spans by decades has become apparent, though the prospect of immortality remains a distant dream.

Left: A scanning electron micrograph showing red blood cells (coloured orange) and white blood cells from a leukaemia patient.

From medicine, we shift the focus to neuroscience and its attempts to understand the human brain, the most complex biological structure in existence. We consider why there are so many more people who are right-handed than left-handed, and how we developed the ability to use complex language, then attempt to unravel the reasons why we all spend so much time asleep. The last two chapters in this section deal with two of the most difficult aspects of neuroscience, looking at the progress we have made in trying to understanding consciousness and how our memory works. Neuroscientists are gradually piecing together the processes in our brains that lead to memory formation and storage – but that phenomenon occurring between our ears, which makes us self-aware, remains a complete mystery.

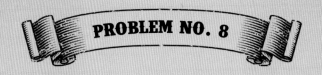

CAN WE FIND A CURE FOR CANCER?

Field: Oncology, epidemiology
Location: Worldwide

Since the beginning of the 1970s, extensive research programmes have greatly improved our understanding of cancer, yet we are still far away from an all-encompassing cure, and it is not apparent that such a breakthrough is even possible.

In many countries around the world, cancer is one of the most common causes of death, often only rivalled by heart disease. This remains the case despite remarkable advances in the diagnosis and treatment of the disease, together with a greater awareness of those lifestyle choices, in particular smoking, which increase the chances of cancer developing.

The principal reason cancer has become such a common cause of death is, paradoxically, because of the successes of medical science and healthcare. Cancer can strike at any age but is much more common in people over the age of 65, and life expectancy in most of the world, with the exception of sub-Saharan Africa, now exceeds this figure. In the more developed regions, life expectancy is now about 80, peaking at 84 in Japan, and, as populations have aged, cancer has become more prevalent. In less developed

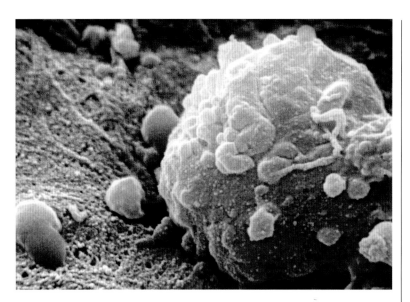

Left: A scanning electron micrograph of a malignant melanoma cell, which can lead to potentially fatal skin cancer.

countries, where life expectancy is not as high, it is also increasing, because healthcare is often not as readily available, and because the sort of preventative measures adopted in more developed countries – such as those aimed at reducing smoking through taxing tobacco and enforcing smoking bans in public places – are not as widespread.

THE DIFFICULTY WITH CANCER

The reason why a cure for cancer has not been found is because it is not a single disease with a single cause. There are well over a hundred different types of cancer, including those named after the parts of the body where they occur, such as lung, breast, prostate and colon cancers, those which form in bone marrow (leukaemias) or white blood cells (lymphomas) and those of the skin, known as melanomas. This is further complicated because the malignant tumours which form as the cancer develops can be very different among people with the same cancer, or even within the same person, making it difficult to develop a single treatment for even one type of the disease – never mind finding a cure for all of them.

HOW CANCER WORKS

Cancer is a consequence of genetic mutations within the DNA of individual cells, which build up over time and can cause those cells to behave abnormally. These mutations are errors that can occur in the DNA sequence when cells divide, and they mostly happen in response to environmental factors, such as exposure to carcinogens or radiation, through, for instance, the chemicals in tobacco smoke or the ultraviolet rays of the Sun. A much smaller proportion of cancers, thought to be up to about ten per cent, are genetically determined, but it is often difficult to be certain of the exact cause, because it could be one of a large number of factors or a combination of any of them.

Damaged cells would normally provoke an immune response from the body to remove them, but cancer cells have the ability to hide from the immune system. These cells then begin to divide uncontrollably, forming tumours, rather than making up tissue

Opposite: The mutant cancer cell in the middle is undergoing cell division, potentially leading to the formation of a tumour.

Below: A patient undergoing radiotherapy, which kills cancer cells but can also affect healthy cells.

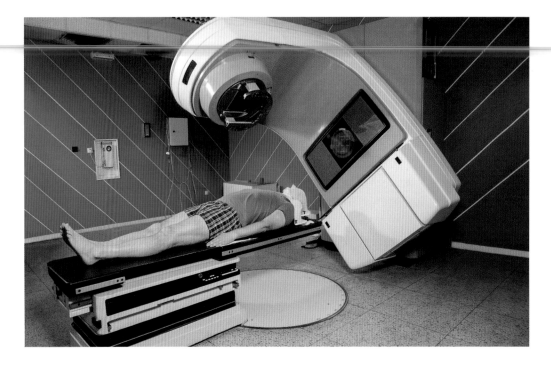

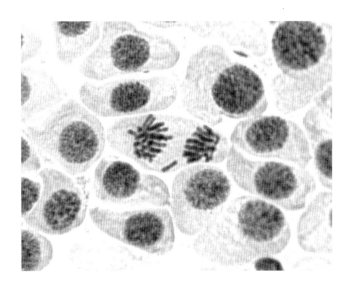

as normal cell division would, and once the cancer has begun in a cell it can also infect those healthy cells that surround the cancer cell. As the infected cells divide, rapid evolution can take place, making the cancer individual to the person in whom it occurs – adding further layers of complication to developing effective treatment. From its beginnings in one part of the body, the cancer can then spread, in a process known as metastasis, and the disruption this causes to normal bodily functions is often what makes cancer fatal.

BEATING CANCER

In the absence of a cure, various treatments that involve getting rid of the cancerous cells can be employed. Tumours can be removed by means of surgery, which is the most effective method if the cancer is detected before it has spread, or the cancer cells can be killed with radiation (radiotherapy) or drugs (chemotherapy). The difficulty with both of these treatments is in specifically targeting the cancer cells while preventing normal cells being killed, while both also come with a range of side effects.

Another type of treatment that has advanced considerably in recent years is immunotherapy, in which the body's own immune system is stimulated so that it kills the cancer cells. The immune system works by producing antibodies that bind to foreign cells in the body; once detected in this way, these cells are then killed and removed. Cancer cells have proteins on their surfaces that effectively switch off this immune response, and immunotherapy works by masking these surface proteins using specific antibodies that can bind to them. In this way, the cancer cell is no longer hidden from the immune system and thus is destroyed. Significant progress has been made in the treatment of some skin cancers in this way, and research is ongoing to extend it to other forms of the disease. But it has also become clear that not all patients respond to it and, as cancer can evolve very quickly, resistance can develop to the particular drugs being used.

In other lines of research, some cancers have been found to be triggered in response to infections by viruses that themselves can be prevented by vaccination, while considerable attention is now being directed towards both the genetic and epigenetic control of those genes in which the cancer-causing mutations occur. In the future, drugs may become available that target these control mechanisms, inhibiting the mutations which lead to cells becoming cancerous without damaging normal cells. In this way, tailor-made gene therapies designed for the individual patient may be developed, or genes could be used in ways that enhance existing treatments, though this is an extremely complicated field and much more research needs to be done.

What has become clear over decades of cancer research is that a single cure is unlikely to be found, unless a spectacular breakthrough is made in which, for instance, a factor common to all cancers is discovered. But advances in treatments are progressively increasing the survival rate for those who contract most forms of cancer. We can also help ourselves by avoiding carcinogens, through paying attention to the advice our doctors give us: stop smoking, don't drink too much alcohol, eat less red meat and more fresh fruit and vegetables, do regular exercise and use sunscreen.

— ALTERNATIVE —
THEORIES

The difficulty of targeting radiotherapy and chemotherapy at cancer cells, without damaging the healthy cells that surround them, limits the dosages that can be used and thereby possibly makes the treatments less effective. An emerging area of research, which has the potential to enable a much more accurate delivery of radiation or drugs, or a combination of the two, is the field of nanomedicine. This is a branch of nanotechnology, which involves manipulating substances at the level of the atom or molecule, and is named after the nanometre, the unit of measurement that is one-billionth of a metre. The idea is to develop nanoparticles that target cancer cells – either as drugs in their own right, which specifically act on or within an individual cell, or as markers that penetrate the cell and draw radiation or chemotherapy drugs towards it instead of towards normal cells. The research is very much in its infancy at the moment, but hopes have been expressed that at some stage in the future it will be possible to design a

Above: Scientists working in orange light at the London Centre for Nanotechnology, using a process sensitive to light with shorter wavelengths.

single drug in this way, which can treat a number of different cancers more effectively than is possible at the moment while, at the same time, having few, if any, side effects. Specific treatments using this form of nanotechnology could be designed for individual patients and the particular form of cancer they have developed. This would provide a powerful new method of treating the disease, with the potential to overcome the ability of new cancers to mutate as they grow.

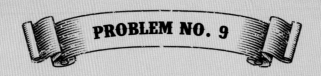

WILL WE EVER DEVELOP A VACCINE FOR HIV?

Field: Virology
Location: Worldwide

In 1983, HIV (human immunodeficiency virus) was found to be the cause of a range of conditions collectively known as AIDS (acquired immune deficiency syndrome). Over 35 million people have since died due to HIV, and the same number live with it.

The high number of HIV cases and deaths worldwide is in part because the antiretroviral drugs that have been available since the mid 1990s, allowing infections to be managed, are not always widely available in certain parts of the world – in particular in Africa, where HIV infection rates are highest. But also, unlike many other viral diseases, attempts to develop a vaccine for HIV have so far been unsuccessful.

Vaccination against a variety of infectious diseases is now such a routine part of healthcare that it is easy to forget how important it has been in the history of medical science. Many millions of deaths have been prevented since the principles of vaccination were established by the English physician Edward Jenner in the late eighteenth century. Jenner had become aware of local knowledge near his home in Gloucestershire; milkmaids who had previously caught cowpox, a relatively mild disease, did not then suffer from the similar but much more serious, and potentially fatal, smallpox. Jenner conducted trials in which he exposed people to cowpox and some weeks later to smallpox, finding that the more serious disease did not develop. It represented the beginning of a long process, which culminated in 1979 when, after a decades-long programme of vaccination, the World Health Organization was able to announce that smallpox had been completely eradicated.

THE SUCCESS OF VACCINES

Great advances in our understanding of how vaccines work were made in the late nineteenth and early twentieth centuries by, among many others, Louis Pasteur, Robert Koch and Paul Ehrlich (the German physician, rather than the American environmentalist of the same name we encountered in 'How can we deal with global population growth?' (page 45)). The way in which the

Below: A nineteenth-century coloured engraving of Edward Jenner vaccinating his own child with cowpox.

immune system works – through the production of antibodies – was discovered, and methods of producing vaccines extended from Jenner's use of a related mild disease to the use of killed or weakened forms of the original infectious agent, allowing vaccines for a greater range of diseases to be developed. Vaccines were developed for one infectious disease after another, perhaps most famously including the vaccine for polio, developed in 1955 by the American virologist Jonas Salk.

THE TROUBLE WITH HIV

In among the remarkable successes, vaccines for a few infectious diseases remain frustratingly out of reach. HIV has the ability to evolve quickly, making it difficult to produce a vaccine that will be – and will remain – effective against all the different strains. A further complication arises because it initially evolved to attack the immune system, which has given the virus a complicated surface structure that enables it to evade detection. Vaccines work by stimulating what is known as the adaptive immune system, the part of the system that can remember the structure of pathogens, so that when these are encountered again the immune response will be enhanced. In the case of HIV, the usual ways of producing a vaccine do not work because it is not detected in the first place, so the immune system is not stimulated.

As if the problem of producing a vaccine was not already complicated enough, further difficulties arise because the two usual methods for producing active agents for vaccines have not worked for HIV. Most vaccines have been developed using either a killed or deactivated (attenuated) version of the pathogen, so that it stimulates the immune system without causing harm. HIV that has been killed does not stimulate an immune response, while the complex structure of the virus means that attempting to deactivate it is difficult. So using an attenuated version would run the risk of infecting the patient.

— ALTERNATIVE —
THEORIES

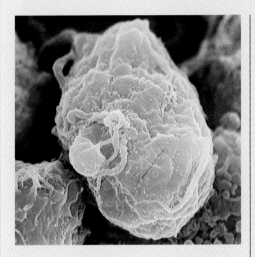

Above: A scanning electron micrograph of the human immunodeficiency virus (visible in the tiny surface bumps).

HIV suppresses the immune system by invading and attacking T cells, which play a crucial role in what is known as cell-mediated immunity. It was thought that, once the virus had invaded a T cell, it replicated and then spread to other T cells through the blood. Recent research has found that it can actually spread much more quickly, by utilising short-lived connections between T cells in order to transfer directly from one cell to another. This may help to explain why those vaccines developed so far have not been very effective, because these have only worked against HIV in the blood, and it may also open up the possibility of new forms of treatment that in some way block this cell-to-cell transmission.

A formidable range of obstacles still exists, but over 30 years of research have provided us with a huge body of knowledge on HIV, leading many scientists to be optimistic about a future cure. In the meantime, advances in the management of the disease mean that those with HIV, with access to the relevant drugs, can expect to lead an almost normal life. Until a vaccine is found, the challenge remains to extend these treatments to as many people as possible.

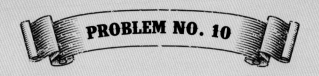

WHAT CAN WE DO ABOUT ANTIBIOTIC RESISTANCE?

Field: Pharmacology, bacteriology
Location: Wherever antibiotics are used

In 2014, the World Health Organization stated that antibiotic resistance was 'happening right now in every region of the world' – leaving us at risk of entering a 'post-antibiotic era', where common infections could once again become fatal.

The WHO's first global report on antibiotic resistance may sound alarmist, but it reflects the crucial role antibiotics have played in treating microbial diseases and infections since first becoming available in the 1930s.

Antibiotics were discovered in 1928 by the Scottish bacteriologist Alexander Fleming while he was working at the St Mary's Hospital Medical School in London. During the First World War he had served as a medic in military hospitals behind the Western Front, where he witnessed the deaths of many soldiers from wounds that had become septic as a consequence of bacterial infections. After the war, Fleming directed his research efforts towards finding better ways of dealing with such infections and, according to his later account, discovered penicillin through sheer good luck. A fungal mould of the genus *Penicillium* had infected a Petri dish containing a bacterial culture, after the spores had apparently blown into Fleming's laboratory through a window that had accidentally been left open. As he was about to throw the Petri dish away, Fleming noticed that the bacteria around the mould had been killed, leading him to isolate the active substance produced by the mould, which he named penicillin.

A MEDICAL REVOLUTION

It took ten years for any serious work to start on developing penicillin into a usable antibiotic and, in the meantime, the German pharmaceutical company Bayer developed sulphonamide antibacterial drugs, sold under the name of Prontosil. The beginning of the Second World War led to renewed interest in penicillin, and a team at Oxford University – led by Howard Florey and including the Jewish, German-born Ernst Chain, who had fled Germany in 1933 to escape persecution – developed a method of producing penicillin for medicinal use. For this work they, together with Fleming, were later awarded the Nobel Prize for medicine.

Above: Sir Alexander Fleming, seen here at work in his laboratory in 1951.

Making enough penicillin for armies during the Second World War proved difficult until deep fermentation was developed in America, coming just in time to provide sufficient supplies for the armed forces during the invasion of Normandy in June 1944. After the war, further research improved penicillin, and other antibiotics were developed, leading to a medical revolution that, coupled with the widespread use of vaccines, has dramatically reduced the impact of fatal or debilitating diseases and infections.

GROWING RESISTANCE

Almost as soon as he began to work on penicillin, Alexander Fleming recognised the potential for bacteria to develop resistance, because of the capacity such microbes have to replicate very rapidly, providing the opportunity for evolution to occur. Should a mutation arise which confers resistance, it can spread quickly – facilitated by the further use of antibiotics, because these would then wipe out any non-resistant bacteria that would otherwise compete with the resistant strain. Despite repeated warnings by Fleming and many others not to misuse antibiotics, it quickly became common practice for doctors to prescribe them for a much wider range of illnesses than they should have, often simply because patients demanded them.

Today, antibiotics are still being given to patients who have colds or flu – viral infections against which such treatments are ineffective – and are also widely used in veterinary medicine as a preventative measure in livestock farming rather than as a treatment for a specific disease. In some countries, antibiotics are also used as growth promoters in livestock, it having been found that animals treated in this way often perform better. About two-thirds of all antibiotics are now used on farms, and while these are different from the ones used to treat people, such use can nevertheless result in a buildup of resistance, which has the potential to transfer to medicinal antibiotics.

Resistance will build up in bacteria even where antibiotics are used responsibly, but the more they are used, the quicker this will happen, so it is vitally important that they are not overprescribed, or misused in livestock farming. Unfortunately, this advice has not always been followed, leading to a number of infectious

Below: A bacterial culture growing in a Petri dish and showing resistance to an antibiotic.

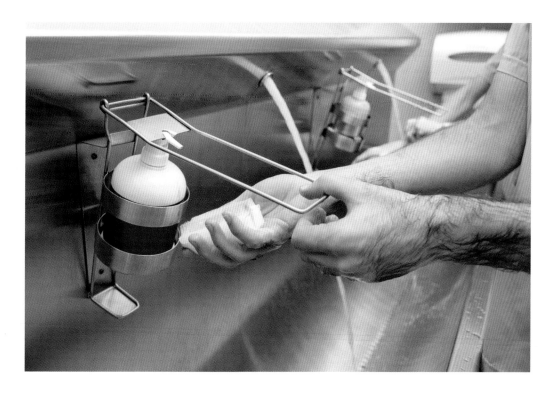

Above: An increased emphasis on hygiene in hospitals has helped to minimise the spread of MRSA.

diseases becoming increasingly difficult to treat. Some of the best-known examples are those particularly associated with hospitals, known in the media as 'superbugs', such as MRSA (methicillin-resistant *Staphylococcus aureus*). These bacteria are not necessarily any more virulent than strains that remain sensitive to antibiotics – the problem being that they are much more difficult to treat, particularly those which have become what is known as multidrug-resistant. Stricter regimes of hygiene in hospitals have been found to minimise the spread of MRSA, but it nevertheless represents a serious and ongoing problem for healthcare.

Multidrug-resistant *Mycobacterium tuberculosis* is another microbe becoming more common worldwide. As its name suggests, this bacterium is responsible for tuberculosis, a potentially fatal infectious disease of the respiratory system, which was thought to be under control through the use of antibiotics until the 1980s, when resistant strains began to emerge. Today, more than 100,000 people are thought to die every year as a consequence of this resistance – many of whom live on the African continent, where treatment may not be available and where, in some cases, those infected already have an immune system weakened by HIV.

DEVELOPING SOLUTIONS

One potential solution to antibiotic resistance would be the regular introduction of new classes of antibiotics to which pathogens have no resistance, but so far this has not happened. Big pharmaceutical companies, responsible for the design and introduction of most new drugs, have been reluctant to invest in developing new antibiotics because it is difficult and expensive, and antibiotics are not very lucrative compared to other classes of drugs. Patients usually only need antibiotics for about a week, and new ones would only remain effective for as long as it took for resistance to build up, which can take just a few years. Drugs for conditions such as heart disease and cancer are often used for long-term treatments so, once pharmaceutical companies have made the initial investment involved in development and clinical trials, they can expect to sell successful drugs for a much longer period.

In its 2014 report, the WHO identified serious gaps in available information on the types of antibiotic resistance occurring globally, which, together with a lack of coordination between countries, was impeding possible responses to what has become a serious problem. As well as stating that increased information gathering and sharing is needed, the report recommended greater government investment in research, and the responsible use of antibiotics in medicine and agriculture. Everybody has a part to play, though, from doctors not overprescribing antibiotics to patients using them exactly as directed.

—ALTERNATIVE—
THEORIES

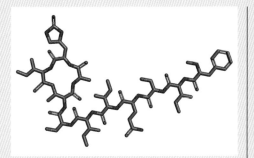

Above: The molecular structure of teixobactin, the first new class of antibiotic to be found in three decades.

In January 2015, researchers at Northeastern University in Boston, Massachusetts, reported that they had discovered a new antibiotic named teixobactin, which they had isolated from the soil bacterium *Eleftheria terrae* through a new culturing method. It was the first new class of antibiotic to be found for almost 30 years, and in tests proved effective against a range of bacteria, including MRSA and *Mycobacterium tuberculosis*, neither of which appeared to develop resistance to it. Teixobactin works by inhibiting the production of those fats that form a constituent part of cell walls and preventing bacteria from growing, while most other antibiotics target proteins in the cell wall or inside the cell to kill fully grown bacteria. The research team thought that *E. terrae* might have developed this function in response to naturally occurring resistance.

If they are correct, resistance to teixobactin is less likely to develop in the first place and, even if it does, will take much longer to build up than resistance against existing antibiotics. Clinical trials should take about five years and, if it passes, the research team predicts that teixobactin could remain effective for over 30 years. Even if teixobactin fails these trials, this new method of culturing soil bacteria in the laboratory can be used to investigate the potential of many other species of bacteria to produce antibiotics. This on its own could lead to a whole new era in the fight against antibiotic resistance.

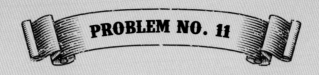

IS IMMORTALITY POSSIBLE?

Field: Biogerontology, geroscience, genetics
Location: Within the bodies of us all

The possibility of stopping or even reversing the ageing process may sound as if it belongs in a science-fiction novel, but cellular senescence, as the ageing of cells is known, is now very much an active area of serious scientific research.

As our understanding of the processes involved in cellular senescence increases, the prospect of being able to extend life expectancy well beyond what it is now has become a real one, leading some scientists to suggest that one day even immortality may become a possibility. As we have already seen, advances in medical science and healthcare have already had a dramatic impact on life expectancy, pushing it up above 80 in much of the developed world. The rate of increase has now slowed, as the sorts of disease that tend to come on in older people, such as cancer and heart disease, have become more prevalent. As discussed in 'Can we find a cure for cancer?' (page 52), genetic mutations during otherwise normal cell division accumulate with age, and even where these do not lead to abnormal cell division and the formation of tumours – as happens with cancer – these mutations appear to be a factor in cellular senescence. As people get older, cells stop dividing, and tissue begins to deteriorate as dead cells are no longer being replaced, leading to an overall decline in the body and its functions, and, ultimately, to death.

CELLULAR SENESCENCE

Chromosomes are structures within the nuclei of cells, made of compacted strands of DNA which replicate during cell division. The tips of the chromosomes consist of repetitive lengths of DNA, known as telomeres, and these function as protective caps comparable to the little plastic sheaths on the end of shoelaces (called aglets) which stop the laces from fraying. Each time the chromosomes of a cell replicate during division, short lengths of DNA at the ends of the telomeres are lost until, after multiple divisions, not enough is left and the cell can no longer divide, so it becomes senescent. But some types of cells possess an enzyme called telomerase which repairs the telomeres after cell division, so these cells could, in theory, continue to replicate indefinitely.

Below: An electron micrograph of human chromosomes. The telomeres have been marked with yellow dye.

One type of cell containing telomerase is the stem cell. In an embryo, stem cells differentiate (or change cell type in order to serve a specialised function) to form all the various tissues and organs of the body as it grows. In adults, stem cells can repair damaged cells. Cancer cells also have the telomerase enzyme, allowing them to continue dividing uncontrollably, forming tumours where normal cells would have

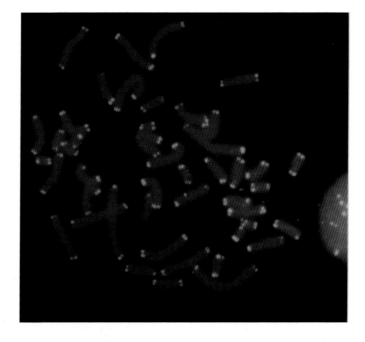

stopped as the telomeres would have run out. Both stem cells and cancer cells could be said to exhibit cellular immortality, while the telomeres in almost all other cells act like a biological clock counting down towards death. The length of these telomeres determines what is known as the Hayflick limit, the number of times a cell can divide before senescence begins – usually about 60 – and named after Leonard Hayflick, who first described the phenomenon in the 1960s.

A direct link between the length of telomeres and the process of ageing has proved difficult to establish because there appear to be numerous other factors involved, not least the accumulation of genetic mutations in DNA over time. But, in theory at least, it may be possible to develop a therapy that can either maintain or replenish the telomeres, potentially extending life for a considerable period. This could not be considered as moving towards immortality, though, unless the therapy also included measures to deal with age-related illnesses. Who, for instance, would want to live forever if most of that time was spent suffering from Alzheimer's disease?

WHAT HAPPENS NEXT

As well as investigating how cells become senescent, a further line of research concerns what happens afterwards. Rather than being removed, as might be expected, senescent cells remain in the body and build up over time. The presence of these cells is thought to have some beneficial functions, playing a role in the repair of damaged tissue, but, while no longer capable of division, they can exude harmful chemicals which damage healthy cells, rather like a bad apple is said to spoil the barrel. Some of these chemicals cause inflammation in the surrounding cells and, as inflammation is a common factor in almost all age-related diseases, research is currently ongoing in an effort to find ways of either removing the senescent cells or preventing them from producing toxic chemicals. Should this be successful, it has the potential to form the basis

— ALTERNATIVE — THEORIES

In experiments conducted on a wide range of organisms, from unicellular yeasts to rhesus monkeys, a substantially reduced diet, involving a calorie intake of less than half the normal, has been shown to lead to a considerable increase in life span – sometimes by as much as 50 per cent. The reasons for this are not known, and similar experiments on human beings would be unethical because of the well-known health impacts of malnutrition, so it is impossible to know if we would live longer as a consequence of calorie restriction. In any case, a lifetime of denying ourselves one of the great pleasures of life, the enjoyment of good food, hardly appears to be a great trade-off for a few extra years.

Above: Misao Okawa, the Japanese woman who was one of only three people to have reached the age of 117.

of a single treatment for a whole range of age-related illnesses – including dementia, heart disease and cancer – which will not only extend our life spans, but also ensure we retain our health as we grow older.

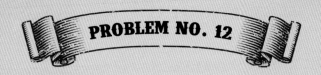
WHY ARE MORE PEOPLE RIGHT-HANDED THAN LEFT-HANDED?

Field: Anatomy, cognitive science, neuroscience, genetics
Location: In our brains and hands

Almost all of us favour the use of one hand over the other, using our preferred side in our everyday life without giving it much thought. Yet in truth, scientists still don't really know why around nine out of ten people are right-handed.

If we were to pause for a moment while chopping vegetables for dinner to consider why we were using our right or left hand, we might conclude that it simply felt like the correct way of doing things, without being able to say why. Scientists who have studied this form of lateralisation, as they would call it, have some theories, but, in reality, they also have no idea at all.

Humans, like most animals, exhibit bilateral symmetry, in that one half of our body looks much the same as the other. Our brains are also divided into two halves, the right and left hemispheres, connected by a structure called the corpus callosum – a bundle of nerves that allows communication between the two. For the most part, the two hemispheres are mirror images of each other,

controlling the same range of functions in the same regions, with the left hemisphere controlling the right side of the body and vice versa – a situation arising as a consequence of the way in which our nervous system is wired up. But our brains also exhibit a certain degree of what neuroscientists call functional asymmetry, because some regions in each hemisphere have specialised functions not mirrored in the other side. As handedness is also asymmetrical, in that many more people are right-handed, it may be linked in some way to these specialised regions of the brain.

Above: Like nine out of ten of us, this young girl is using her right hand to draw.

LANGUAGE AND THE LEFT HEMISPHERE

Handedness is often said to have a connection to the use of language, which may appear a rather random attribution but is based on the fact that, for the majority of us, our ability to speak is associated with two specialised regions in the left hemisphere, known as Broca's area and Wernicke's area. Since the use of language requires a high degree of mental and physical agility, it is thought that the hemisphere primarily concerned with controlling language becomes the dominant hemisphere of the two – causing the side of the body controlled by this hemisphere to be favoured. Studies have found that almost all right-handed people make use of the left hemisphere for language, but the theory is somewhat undermined by the fact that the language skills of most left-handers are not controlled by their right hemispheres. In fact, for about 60 per cent of left-handers, language is also controlled in the left hemisphere, suggesting either that the relationship between language and handedness is a complicated one, or that the two abilities are not actually connected at all.

AN EVOLUTIONARY ADVANTAGE

A further theoretical connection between language and handedness has been proposed, which suggests that the two evolved at the same time in early humans – perhaps coming together as our ancestors began to walk upright and use their hands in more specialised ways, for instance for making and using tools, while at the same time living in more complex social situations, requiring greater communication skills. Perhaps there was also an evolutionary pressure in our distant past, which in some way favoured right-handers while at the same time providing conditions in which a smaller number of left-handers also prospered.

One line of thought on the matter uses game theory, drawing on the fact that left-handers in some sports today can have a slight competitive advantage over their right-handed opponents. In tennis, lefties can benefit from right-handers being more accustomed to playing other right-handers, while the same applies to boxers who fight in the southpaw stance – though the situation in which an advantage of this sort would have benefited our distant ancestors is far from obvious.

If anything, our knowledge of the role played by genetics is even less clear. Recent research has shown that handedness is

— ALTERNATIVE —
THEORIES

In 1979, two of the leading figures in the field of evolutionary biology, Stephen Jay Gould and Richard Lewontin, borrowed the word 'spandrel' from the architecture of cathedrals. They used it to describe a trait that first appears in an organism as a by-product of the evolution of a different trait – rather than being an adaptive response in its own right. Gould and Lewontin specifically referred to St Mark's Basilica in Venice, describing the curved triangular pieces of masonry where the circular dome of the cathedral rests on its rectangular basilica – known to architects as a particular type of spandrel, called a pendentive – as by-products of fitting a dome and a rectangle together, rather than being designed to be that shape for artistic purposes by the architect. The

Above: The triangular spandrels above the arches in St Mark's Basilica, Venice.

concept of biological spandrels proved controversial, and remains a disputed one today, but it could explain why it is so difficult to establish why we favour one hand over the other. There is no explanation because there is no reason. It just happened that way.

a complicated affair, involving up to 40 genes, one in which environmental, or epigenetic, factors most likely contribute as well. In reality, this particular problem may never be solved. Perhaps we should just get on with whatever tasks we have set ourselves, using whichever hand we choose, and not worry about it too much.

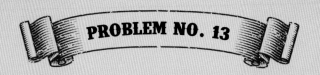

WHAT IS THE ORIGIN OF LANGUAGE?

Field: Linguistics, cognitive science, neuroscience, anatomy
Location: In every culture around the world

Our ability to communicate our thoughts in complex words and sentences is unique, often cited as an accomplishment that sets us apart from other animals. Yet we still know very little about when and how we came to acquire this remarkable skill.

The main problem in the study of the origin of language is the lack of empirical evidence – because, as Steven Pinker, one of the leading scholars in the field, puts it, languages don't leave fossils. To investigate further, then, we have to take an indirect approach by making inferences from what does survive in the archaeological record, and from what we know about our evolutionary history. We can also study languages as they exist today through linguistics, and use the knowledge we have gained through cognitive science and neuroscience of the ways in which our brains work in relation to language. When you add into the mix the contributions of anthropologists, psychologists, philosophers and many others from different disciplines, all approaching the subject from their own perspectives, what you end up with is an enormous number of theories and very little consensus. This makes for some lively debates, but leaves the subject in such a confused state that it is almost impossible to envisage a time when a clear understanding will emerge.

UNIVERSAL GRAMMAR

One of the leading figures in linguistics is Noam Chomsky, who has become as well known for his political activism as for his scholarship. One of his contributions to the study of language was to develop the theory that its acquisition in young children is an innate ability, and that all of us have an inbuilt 'universal grammar' which facilitates language learning, and which underlies the specific language we first learn. This, as cognitive scientists would put it, is hard-wired into our brains, meaning that it is a faculty determined by our genes, which enables young children to begin to construct sentences out of the words they have picked up without having to be taught. Ever since these ideas were first put forward by Chomsky in the 1960s, a furious debate has raged between those who support his view, including Steven Pinker, and

Below: Noam Chomsky, whose theory of universal grammar has been highly influential in the field of linguistics.

those who think that language and grammar are not innate but are instead learned through social interaction.

If we accept Chomsky's argument that language is innate, then it follows that either it first began as a consequence of a specific genetic mutation at some point in our evolutionary history, which is Chomsky's view, or that it arose more gradually in our early evolutionary history, as our ancestors diverged from other primates. Chimpanzees, our closest living relatives, communicate with a wide array of vocalisations and gestures, but do not appear to have the ability to put these together in a meaningful way to express more complicated concepts than what is immediately on their minds. This implies that language began at some point after the human and chimpanzee evolutionary lines diverged about 6 million years ago, providing us with a top limit on the date we acquired language, because it must have happened after the split occurred. As language is a universal feature in every known culture around the world, it must also have arisen before humans began to migrate out of Africa about 60,000 years ago – giving us a time frame of between 6 million years ago and 60,000 years ago, during which language evolved, and also the very approximate location of somewhere on the African continent.

GENETICS AND EVOLUTION

In 2001, research carried out on people with verbal dyspraxia, an inherited speech disorder, resulted in the discovery of a gene, named

FOXP2, which appears to be important in the development of language. Children with verbal dyspraxia cannot acquire language in the usual way, and often suffer from severe speech impediments. They know what they are trying to say and have no physical constraints, but their brains are incapable of processing and transmitting the information to their vocal apparatus. This is thought to be caused by a mutation in the FOXP2 gene, demonstrating its importance in the use of language, and leading to speculation that slight differences between it and a very similar gene found in chimpanzees may represent an important stage in our evolutionary history.

Above: A reconstruction of a Neanderthal man at the Neanderthal Museum in Düsseldorf, Germany.

Opposite: Chimpanzees like this one express anger through vocalising, but they cannot put concepts together to form a language.

A project sequencing the genome of Neanderthals at the Max Planck Institute for Evolutionary Anthropology in Leipzig, Germany, has shown that Neanderthals also possessed the FOXP2 gene, indicating that they had some facility for language, even if this does not prove that they used it in the way we do. Neanderthals diverged from the same evolutionary line as anatomically modern humans about 350,000 years ago, so if it can be shown that they did communicate like us then it could also show that language had already evolved by that date – though the situation is somewhat complicated by another finding by the Neanderthal genome project, which indicated that some interbreeding occurred with modern humans.

In a different line of research, a study of the diversity of phonemes in a number of different African languages that are thought to have very ancient origins, such as the !Xun language of southern Africa, was used to calculate a date for the origin of language. Phonemes are the actual sounds we make when we articulate the vowels and consonants that make up words, and have been found to accumulate at a predictable rate in a language as it evolves. !Xun has 141 phonemes – including characteristic clicks denoted with an exclamation mark in the written language – compared to about 44 in English. The study used the predictable rate of phoneme creation to count backwards and, in this way, came to the conclusion that language evolved between 350,000 and 150,000 years ago.

So if we accept the findings of these two studies, which both come with a long list of qualifications, then it follows that the use of language began with *Homo heidelbergensis*, the common ancestor we share with Neanderthals, and that it developed shortly before our evolutionary lines diverged 350,000 years ago. No clear evidence exists to suggest that *H. heidelbergensis* either did or did not have the ability to use language, and many scholars in the field, including Noam Chomsky, think it is of much more recent origins. But then again, if language really is a defining feature of humanity, it would not be unreasonable to propose that it has been with us right from the beginning.

WHAT WE CAN SAY

With such uncertainty over when languages evolved, it is hardly surprising to find that the answer to the more difficult question of how it happened is even more unclear, and there now appear to be almost as many theories attempting to explain this as there are researchers in the field. One theory, for instance, suggests that language first arose out of the sort of gestures we see today in chimpanzees, rather than as an adaptation of vocal sounds. As we began to make more use of our hands to hold tools, so the theory goes, we had to find other ways of communicating, and began to use our voices to express the same thoughts as had previously been communicated with our hands. Alternatively, language could have arisen out of the sounds mothers made to comfort their babies, before being extended to include other relatives. Or, it could have coevolved along with a number of other characteristic human traits that required complex interactions, such as ritualistic behaviour like burying the dead. It could have been a consequence of our beginning to live in larger social groups and interact in different ways, or as an evolutionary response to a specific set of environmental or cultural circumstances not immediately apparent to us today, but which selected people better able to communicate.

A different approach looks at the evolution of the anatomical features that allow us to produce the variety of sounds required for speech. Our vocal tract is somewhat different from that of chimpanzees, particularly in the position of the larynx, or voice

Below: An illustration of humans working iron. Language may have developed for communication as we increasingly used our hands for holding tools.

box, which is lower down in the throat. This descended larynx, as it is known, allows us to move our tongue more freely than chimps, and the tongue itself is larger and flatter to allow us greater flexibility in the sounds we produce. We also exhibit different muscle development in our chest, giving us better breath control and allowing us to produce the long and continuous sounds required for language, rather than the shorter and more sporadic noises made by chimps.

It used to be thought that the evolution of features such as the descended larynx was a prerequisite for the development of speech, until subsequent research showed that chimpanzees actually have the ability to lower their larynx when they make certain vocalisations and, in fact, several other animals also have a permanently descended larynx – demonstrating that anatomical features on their own are not enough to explain the emergence of language. A more likely scenario is that the genetic, cognitive and anatomical features required for language evolved together. But, whatever the truth of the matter, the ability to communicate through language has proved to be one of the key adaptations in the extraordinary success of our species, which has seen us spread out and colonise almost all of the habitable parts of the world. It may only be our own hubris that allows us to think of our use of language as setting us apart from and above other animals, but, then again, we are the only species capable of expressing the concept of hubris, so perhaps we have some grounds for a little pride in ourselves. We may not know exactly how we came to acquire such a talent, and it is far from clear that we will ever get to the bottom of the matter, but one thing it is possible to say with certainty is that once we started talking, we never stopped.

— ALTERNATIVE —
THEORIES

Above: Two young girls enjoying a private joke, communicating in a way that can strengthen the ties between us.

One of the things chimpanzees like to do when they have some time on their hands is sit around together and groom each other. People do a similar sort of thing, except, rather than grooming, we chat about what we and everybody else we know has been doing. Rather than this being a rather frivolous by-product of our ability to talk, the anthropologist and primatologist Robin Dunbar thinks that this sort of gossiping is one of the principal reasons why we began to use language in the first place. Vocal grooming, as Dunbar calls it, can bring us closer together, allowing us to get to know each other better, and strengthening the ties between us. These are important aspects of living together in an extended social group that includes people who are not necessarily related to each other, as our distant ancestors began to do. Vocal grooming also has the advantage of leaving our hands free to do other things. Another theory along the same lines suggests that language evolved as a consequence of our proclivity for telling stories, a feature of every culture around the world. Like every other theory on our acquisition of language, there is no way of testing whether we first began to speak so that we could gossip about people and tell stories to each other – but this might help to explain the ability many of us exhibit to talk at great length about nothing in particular.

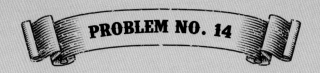

WHY DO WE SLEEP?

Field: Neuroscience, somnology, oneirology
Location: Inside our heads

We sleep when we get tired, to rejuvenate ourselves and replenish our energy. What puzzles scientists is why we enter into a significantly altered state of consciousness to do this, rather than going through these processes while awake.

Before the development of electroencephalography (EEG) in the 1920s, research into our sleeping habits was based on the assumption that very little happened in our brains when we were asleep. EEG, which measures the electrical activity in our brains, showed that this was anything but the case, and that, during certain periods of sleep, our brains can be at least as active as when we are awake. This is REM (rapid eye movement) sleep, first described in the 1950s, which, as the name suggests, is characterised by the eyes twitching repeatedly behind the eyelids. Subsequent research has shown that as we sleep, our brains go through four phases – indicated by different wavelengths of electrical signals recorded by EEG – and these phases are repeated in regular cycles, each lasting about 90 minutes, over the course of a night's sleep.

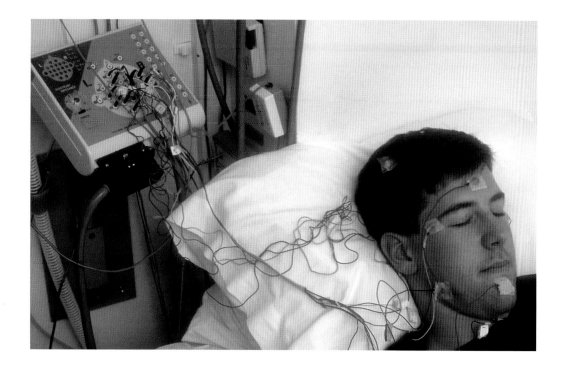

The first three phases are non-REM sleep, in which our brain waves slow down as we go from the initial stage of going to sleep, to light sleep, and then to a deeper sleep, known as slow-wave or phase-three sleep. The brain waves associated with these three phases are known as alpha, beta and delta waves respectively. Then, after slow-wave sleep, we enter REM sleep, in which the much faster theta brain waves are produced. Here, the heartbeat and breathing rates slow down, and almost all of our muscles become paralysed. It is during this phase that dreaming occurs – though we can also dream during slow-wave sleep – and a lack of dreaming has been found to impair our ability to learn and retain memories. As well as these effects, sleep deprivation in general can have a range of impacts – most obviously by making us feel tired and lethargic with a reduced attention span, but it can also lead to an overall unwell feeling, and appears to play a role in the onset of a number of mental health issues, obesity, diabetes and a wide range of other health problems.

Above: A subject connected to an EEG machine to record his brain activity while he is sleeping.

THEORIES OF SLEEP

Sleep, then, clearly plays an important role in keeping us healthy and maintaining our bodies, but that does not explain why we spend almost a third of our lives in what amounts to an unconscious state. One theory suggests that being asleep for long periods is a way of conserving energy while we are going through the processes required to keep us healthy. In diurnal animals such as ourselves – that is, ones that are mainly active during the day – it may be a sensible strategy to be as inactive as possible at night, because there is little that can be accomplished in the dark. As well as using less energy, sleeping somewhere sheltered provides protection from predators and insulation from the cold, which, for us, must have been important while living on the savannahs of Africa, where it is hot during the day but where temperatures can drop dramatically at night.

An alternative theory is based on the notion that, as there is so much activity going on in the brain while we are asleep, then there must be something happening to make this worthwhile. One idea is that our brains process and consolidate the memories we make during the day while we are asleep. The brain is thought to sift through these memories at night, when no more are being made, strengthening some and moving them to other parts of the brain to be stored – in the process, maintaining the capacity for new memories to be made the following day. This idea is supported by research showing that stronger memories form if we sleep between acts of learning and attempting to recall what we have learned, and by the memory loss observably caused by sleep deprivation.

In other research, it has been found that the waste products that tend to accumulate during the day in the brain and central nervous system are removed during sleep, through what is known as the glymphatic clearance pathway. This provides support for the idea of sleep being restorative, but when all of the lines of research are considered together, it begins to look as if there are multiple

— ALTERNATIVE
THEORIES

Above: 'To sleep, perchance to dream', in the words of Shakespeare's Hamlet in his famous speech. Here a woman takes a nap on a train.

Sigmund Freud thought that the purpose of sleep was to allow us to dream, and that the content of these dreams is an expression of wish fulfilment that may be repressed when we are awake. In Freud's view, the interpretation of dreams offers a way to understand what is going on in the unconscious mind, without being hindered by what he called the superego – the part of us made up of culturally acquired feelings such as guilt and shame, which get in the way of what we really want.

Neuroscientists today don't support Freud's ideas, instead suggesting that dreams may play a role in memory consolidation, or act as a mental rehearsal that we go through in order to deal with difficult situations when they crop up in our lives.

functions to sleep, rather than a single overriding purpose. During the hours of sleep, when we are safe and warm, tucked up in bed, we are taking the opportunity to rest and restore ourselves, and strengthen the memories we made during the day at a time when we are not being bothered by anything. While we are going through these important processes, we are not using up any more energy than is absolutely necessary.

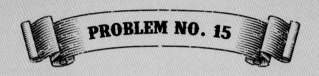

CAN CONSCIOUSNESS BE EXPLAINED BY SCIENCE?

Field: Neuroscience, cognitive science, philosophy
Location: Inside our heads somewhere

One of the most notoriously difficult problems in science to crack is, rather ironically, the one that is closest to home. This is the challenge of understanding our own consciousness.

Put simply, understanding our consciousness involves finding an answer to the apparently intractable question of how the chemical and neurological processes occurring within our bodies lead to the senses of perception and awareness with which we experience the world around us. Up until relatively recently, scientists as a whole were reluctant to engage with the subject of consciousness, apparently preferring to leave it entirely to philosophers. The religions of the world and the ancient Greek philosophers were prepared to address the issue, but the first to consider what has become known as the mind–body problem in a modern philosophical sense was René Descartes in the first half of the seventeenth century. He argued that the mind was not a physical entity and that it was separated from the body, which he described as being like a machine that was controlled by the mind. Cartesian dualism, as this view is called, proved to be enormously influential and was one of the reasons why scientists were reluctant to get involved with the question, because, if the mind is non-physical, then it cannot be studied using empirical methods.

One way of overcoming the problem created by Cartesian dualism is to reject the idea that the mind and body are separate in the first place. This is known as monism and, in one form or another, is largely the position taken by most philosophers of the mind today, together with those scientists who are actually prepared to engage with the philosophical aspects of the study of consciousness. Needless to say, the way in which philosophers describe the concept of monism is a great deal more complicated and involved than is described here, but in essence it at least provides a philosophical stance by which consciousness can be investigated, even if it does not actually advance that study very much on its own.

Below: An illustration showing two ways of seeing a tree: as a monist (top) and as a dualist (bottom).

THE HARD PROBLEM

Over the past few decades, philosophers and scientists have begun to engage with each other more fully than in the past, in the realisation that moving the study of consciousness forward will most likely require input from both sides, and perhaps even an entirely new way of approaching the subject. In part, this involves specifying exactly which questions science is actually attempting to answer. One of the best-known examples of this has been provided by the Australian philosopher David Chalmers, who distinguishes between what he calls the easy problems and the hard problem of consciousness. The easy

problems are those which can be addressed by science as it stands, and concern those processes occurring in the brain and central nervous system which can be detected and measured – or, at least, may well be in the not-too-distant future, as the technology to investigate such mechanisms advances. Examples include how memories are created, stored and retrieved (see page 92), and how our brains deal with a situation in which we are required to make a decision. In both cases it is possible to monitor what is happening in the brain, but much more difficult to understand how these changes relate to the phenomenon of being conscious.

The hard problem is much the same as the mind–body problem, in that it involves explaining how the physical processes of the brain result in consciousness. According to Chalmers, it is distinct from the easy problems because it requires an explanation of a subjective experience that is unique to the individual having that experience. One way of thinking about it was articulated by the American philosopher Thomas Nagel, who posed the question, 'What is it like to be a bat?' We have, of course, not the slightest idea of what it is like to be a bat – the point being that if we were able to work out all the electrochemical processes going on in a bat's brain, we might get to know a great deal more about bats than we do at the moment, but we would still have no idea what it is like to experience the world from a bat's point of view.

Not all philosophers accept that the hard problem exists in the way Chalmers and Nagel suggest – among them Daniel Dennett, who argues that, as neuroscience increases our knowledge of how the brain works, we are gradually getting closer to understanding consciousness, even if there is a long way to go. This has been likened to a computer engineer assembling a computer from its constituent parts, so that once it is put together correctly and switched on, it will become apparent how the internal structure relates to the overall functioning of the computer. Needless to say, we are nowhere near understanding how all the functions of the

— ALTERNATIVE
THEORIES

At the University of Wisconsin-Madison, the Italian neuroscientist Giulio Tononi has been working on a theory of what consciousness actually is and how it can be measured. This is called the integrated information theory, which, rather than attempting to understand how the functioning of the brain leads to consciousness, takes the approach of starting with consciousness to identify its properties and, from there, working out what physical mechanisms are necessary to account for these properties. According to Tononi, two of the principal properties needed for a system to be conscious are that it receives information and that it integrates that information together into a unified whole.

Above: The University of Wisconsin–Madison, where the neuroscientist Giulio Tononi has been conducting theoretical research on consciousness.

Clearly there are many more aspects to consciousness, but here we have the beginnings of a way in which it can be quantified and studied, which may ultimately lead to an understanding of what consciousness is.

brain work, but if this analogy proves to be accurate, then at least there is a possibility that we will be able to unravel one of the great mysteries of science at some point in the future.

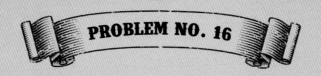

PROBLEM NO. 16

HOW ARE MEMORIES MADE AND STORED?

Field: Neuroscience
Location: In the hippocampus, cerebral cortex and other parts of the brain

Over the past few decades, remarkable progress has been made in working out how chemical changes in the brain are involved in the creation and storage of memories, but we still have a very long way to go before we fully understand how memory works.

In 2000, the Nobel Prize for medicine was awarded to the American neurophysiologist Eric Kandel for his decades-long research into the biochemical basis of memory creation in the California sea slug (*Aplysia californica*). The entire nervous system of a sea slug is composed of about 20,000 nerve cells, or neurons, arranged in ten so-called ganglia – making the creatures easier to study than the human brain, which has 100 billion neurons, each of which is capable of forming thousands of connections to other neurons through what are known as synapses. Synapses are the endings of neurons, where nerve impulses that have travelled along the neurons are converted into biochemicals known as neurotransmitters. These then initiate a series of chemical changes in the synapses – in the gaps between two adjoining neurons, and then in the synapses of the next neurons – which culminates in the nerve impulses being transmitted from one neuron to the next.

THE MEMORY OF A SEA SLUG

Sea slugs are some of the simplest animals that are capable of learning, which means that they can retain memories in response to stimuli. The California sea slug is a particularly large example with correspondingly large neurons, making its neurology easier to study. Kandel was attempting to find evidence to support the theory, first proposed by the Canadian psychologist Donald Hebb in 1949, that in the process of learning the connections between neurons at the synapses are strengthened by increased activity, in a process known to neuroscientists as long-term potentiation. According to the theory, a particular act of learning creates a specific neural pathway, which is then reinforced the more times that it is activated. If that pathway is subsequently not used, the connections between the synapses gradually begin to weaken in what is known as long-term depression. By isolating ganglia of sea slugs and then subjecting these to repeated stimuli of the type that is known to cause the animals to withdraw their gills, Kandel was able to show that these groups of neurons began to exhibit habituation, a simple form of learning. This then allowed him to

Above: The California sea slug has a simple nervous system and large neurons well suited to neurological study.

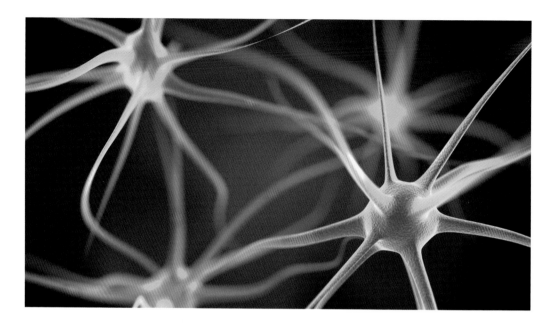

analyse the biochemical changes that had taken place in the sea slugs during the process.

Above: An illustration showing how neurons connect to one another in the brain.

The details of the biochemistry revealed by Kandel are extremely complicated, but in a nutshell it involves a nerve impulse causing the release of the neurotransmitter serotonin into the gap between synapses, which then initiates a chain of reactions controlled by enzymes that ultimately leads to the formation of proteins. More serotonin released as a result of repeated firing of the neurons causes more proteins to be synthesised, and the synapses to become stronger. Some aspects of this process have been found to be genetically based, occurring in the nuclei of neurons and involving changes in the way genes are expressed, though exactly how this happens is not currently very well understood.

FROM SEA SLUGS TO PEOPLE

There is, of course, an enormous difference between the ganglia of sea slugs and the brains of human beings, but both are composed of neurons that have essentially the same structure, so it is reasonable to suggest that the molecular changes in memory formation described by Kandel remain much the same in humans. What is not the same is the nature of memory itself, which is, needless to say, much more complicated in humans than in sea slugs. One way of considering our memories is in terms of the creation of long-term and short-term memories, while another way is to distinguish between implicit memory, the sort involved in learning skills like riding a bike, which, once learned, no longer require a conscious effort to use, and explicit memory, concerning conscious creation, storage and recall.

After his research on sea slugs, Kandel turned his attention to memory formation in the brains of mammals. Numerous other researchers around the world have also been working in the same field, and in recent years a number of major advances have been made. In 2008, for instance, a team of researchers at the University of Alabama in Tuscaloosa were able to watch the formation of proteins in the neurons of rats' brains in response to a memorable event, tracing the initial changes to the hippocampus in the middle of the brain immediately after the event, and then to the outer cerebral cortex a week later, where these memories appeared to have become permanent. The team suggested they had witnessed short-term memories being created in the hippocampus and then observed those same memories after they had been converted into long-term memories and stored in the cortex.

In a 2014 study on rats, neuroscientists at the University of California in San Diego demonstrated the actual process of long-term potentiation for the first time, using a technique called optogenetics. This involves implanting a light-sensitive gene into the neurons of the brain, which can then be monitored. As the rats were subjected to particular stimuli that caused a learning response, the team found that they could not only create memories through long-term potentiation, but also then switch those memories off again as a consequence of long-term depression.

THE MOMENT A MEMORY FORMS

The obvious problem of not being able to use such invasive techniques to investigate memory in humans has restricted research. Recent work, published in July 2015 – a collaborative effort between neuroscientists at the University of Leicester in Britain and University College, Los Angeles – has managed to get around this problem by studying epilepsy patients undergoing brain surgery. The researchers could implant electrodes in the brains of their subjects – with their consent, of course – that could trace the creation of a memory within a single neuron, without causing the patients any harm. They achieved this by showing participants a photograph of a person they recognised, usually members of their families or a well-known actor such as Jennifer Aniston or Clint Eastwood, and then showing them another image of the same person superimposed over a well-known place. When the subjects were then shown a picture of the landmark on its own, it was found that the exact neuron that had fired when the participant was shown, for instance, Clint Eastwood, also fired when just shown the place.

The team from Leicester and UCLA had witnessed, for the first time, the precise moment when a memory is formed in a single neuron in the human brain. It is without doubt an important step in understanding human memory, but it also makes clear how much is yet to be understood. We are still a long way from understanding how memories are transferred from the hippocampus to the cortex, or by what means memories are selected to be stored rather than discarded. And we know almost nothing about the process of bringing long-term memories to mind. Nevertheless, innovative research is progressing all the time, so it is possible to foresee a time in the future when we will have a reasonably complete picture of the entire process.

— ALTERNATIVE —
THEORIES

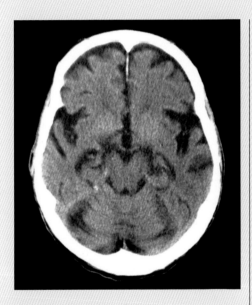

Above: A CT scan of a patient suffering from Alzheimer's disease. The dark areas are where the tissue has atrophied.

The more we understand how memory functions in healthy brains, the better chance we have of being able to treat people who have experienced the sort of brain injury or disease that affects the memory. One of the symptoms of post-traumatic stress disorder is memory loss, and this may be associated with physiological changes that occur in the hippocampus. A study of Vietnam veterans with PTSD found many of them showed atrophy in the hippocampus, and this may be linked to the overproduction of stress hormones such as cortisol, which is regulated by that region of the brain.

Age-related memory loss is becoming more widespread as people live longer. This is mostly a consequence of cells in the brain dying and not being replaced, as happens in the rest of the body as it gets older, but it can be a symptom of the onset of dementia, of which Alzheimer's disease is by far the most common type. The causes of Alzheimer's disease are not well understood, and there is no treatment that stops it, but the earlier it is diagnosed, the more effectively it can be managed. An early sign of the disease is short-term memory loss, so the more we know about this, and about the relationship between memory and dementia in general, the quicker we will be able to diagnose it.

EARTH SCIENCES

D etermining what the interior of the Earth is like is by no means easy, simply because we cannot see it. We have had to find indirect ways of describing what cannot be observed, and, in the opening pages of this chapter, we look at what such research can tell us about the centre of our planet and its magnetic field, which, on a number of occasions in the past, has reversed – so that the North and South Poles have switched around. From the centre of the Earth we move up to its surface, to consider the theory of plate tectonics. Since it was first proposed in the 1960s, it has revolutionised the study of geology, but, even though our knowledge is steadily increasing, we still do not know how the plates formed

Left: Lava reaching the Pacific Ocean from the Hawaiian volcano Kilauea, one of the most active volcanoes in the world.

in the first place. The movement of these plates is what causes earthquakes, and we discuss why all attempts to predict these catastrophic events have so far been unsuccessful.

Water is, of course, essential for life, but, as important as it is to us, we currently don't know how so much of it ended up on the surface of the Earth. As well as considering this aspect of the early history of our planet, we also take a look at the reasons why the last ice age came to an end, and what the science of climatology can tell us about the climate change we are experiencing today. It continues to be the subject of vigorous debate, but is climate change a natural phenomenon, or is it something we have brought on ourselves?

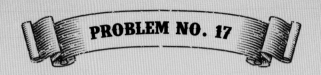
WHAT IS AT THE CENTRE OF THE EARTH?

Field: Geophysics, mineral physics, seismology
Location: The ground beneath our feet

We know more about the composition of the Sun than we do about what is at the centre of the Earth, 6,300 km (4,000 miles) beneath our feet.

The Sun may be 150 million km (93 million miles) away, but at least we can see it. This allows us to analyse the wavelengths of light and other forms of electromagnetic radiation it emits using spectroscopy, from which we can derive its density and mass, as well as its chemical composition. It is, of course, impossible to investigate the centre of the Earth in this way, so we have had to adopt more indirect methods and then infer what it is like below us without being able to say for certain.

In the novel *Journey to the Centre of the Earth*, first published in 1864, Jules Verne imagined that his three protagonists could travel into the depths of the planet by climbing down the inside of an Icelandic volcano. The three heroes have all sorts of adventures underground, but these would have been minor inconveniences compared to what we now know they would have encountered. The temperature at the centre is thought to approach 6,000°C

(10,800°F), about the same as the surface of the Sun, and the pressure is about three million times more than that above ground. In fact, the deepest we have so far been able to drill into the Earth's crust, the thin surface layer of solid rock on which we live, is 12.5 km (slightly less than 8 miles), beyond which the pressure and heat prevent further drilling.

MAPPING THE CORE

The internal structure of the Earth beyond the crust has been mapped by recording seismic waves generated by earthquakes, which pass right through the planet. These waves are of two different types, known as pressure waves (P-waves) and shear waves (S-waves), which are recorded as seismograms by a network of sensors positioned around the world – many of which were first installed during the Cold War to detect and monitor nuclear weapons tests. S-waves can travel through solids but not liquids, while P-waves can travel through both, so, when an earthquake occurs, seismograms show different patterns depending on the nature of the material the waves have passed through. Sensors directly on the other side of the world from an earthquake don't

Below: A seismometer recording S-waves and P-waves caused by an earthquake to produce a seismograph.

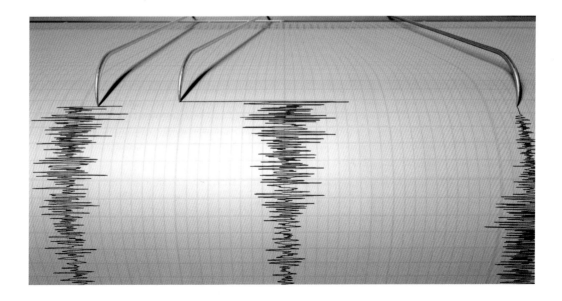

record any S-waves, indicating that the outer core of the earth is liquid and enabling us to deduce its diameter to be roughly 2,900 km (1,800 miles). P-waves travel at different speeds through solids and liquids, so observing the pattern and timing of these waves, detected by the sensors, allows us to map the inner core, showing it to be solid and about 1,220 km (760 miles) across.

The core has been shown to be composed predominantly of iron, together with some nickel and much smaller amounts of heavy metals, oxygen and silicon. This can be inferred from calculations of the mass and density of the Earth, together with our knowledge of the composition of the crust, and of meteorites that have hit the planet. The Earth is actually much heavier than would be expected if its composition were the same as the crust all the way through, showing that the interior must be made up of denser material. Our planet first formed out of interstellar dust and gas about 4.6 billion years ago – shortly after the Sun and along with the other planets in our solar system, as all of these components came under gravitational forces. The heavier materials, such as those containing iron and nickel, gradually sank towards the centre once the Earth had formed, to make up the majority of its core.

Meteorites are composed of the same material that came together to form the solar system, so analysing the composition

Key
1. Crust
2. Upper mantle
3. Lower mantle
4. Outer core
5. Inner core

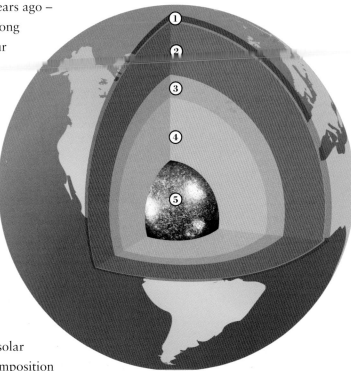

of what is left of meteorites that have hit the Earth shows us what this material was originally like, before gravity got to work on it. These meteorites contain a much greater proportion of iron than is now found in the crust, so we can infer that most of it sank to the centre and that the core must be largely composed of it. Other heavy metals found in meteorites but rare in the crust must also have sunk – including iridium, the presence of which at the surface, as we saw in 'Why did the dinosaurs die out?' (page 24), indicates an impact event.

Above: A fragment recovered in Mexico of the Allende meteorite, which broke up in the Earth's atmosphere in February 1969.

INSIDE THE CORE

Since its formation, the core has radiated heat and, as a consequence, has been cooling very slowly from the centre outwards. This is how the solid inner core is thought to have formed, because under such extreme pressure, iron crystallises out – which means that it freezes, even though the temperature is 6,000°C (10,800°F). As the cooling process continues, the inner core gets bigger, and it is now thought that over the past 500 million years, an innermost core has begun to form within it. The reason why this is happening is not known, though geophysicists have speculated it may have something to do with fluctuations in the crystalline structure of iron in different parts of the inner core.

Opposite: The Earth's internal structure, showing the inner core, outer core, lower mantle, upper mantle and crust.

Attempting to investigate how iron behaves under extreme conditions of temperature and pressure is extremely difficult, and involves using a diamond anvil cell. This is an instrument that squeezes a very small sample of iron between the tips of two crystals of diamond – the hardest known substance – and then heats up the sample with a laser to the temperature of the Earth's core. The structure of iron under these conditions can then be investigated using techniques such as X-ray crystallography, which has shown that iron forms into long thin crystals, orientated in a north-to-south direction. This technique is also the way in which the temperature of the inner core has been calculated, based on the observed melting point of iron samples at very high pressure.

Our understanding of what is going on at the centre of the Earth is expanding all the time, even if much of the knowledge we have gained is theoretical in nature and there is still a great deal more left to discover. One line of ongoing research, for instance, suggests that the inner core is rotating slightly faster than the rest of the planet, doing an extra rotation about every 360 years, and that it is divided into two hemispheres, so that it gives the impression of being a separate planet within the Earth. Explaining these features, and many others besides, will require more of the same sort of innovative science that has been used to discover what we already know about our planet's interior. We may never be able to do what Jules Verne envisaged and actually travel to the centre of the Earth, but we can still discover a great deal about what is going on in the ground beneath our feet.

Below: A beamline at the European Synchrotron Radiation Facility in Grenoble, where scientists attempt to understand conditions at the Earth's core.

— ALTERNATIVE —
THEORIES

The prevailing theory of how the Earth's core formed is that iron sank to the centre at an early stage in the development of the planet. This would have occurred before the solid rocky mantle formed, because iron does not readily pass through the silicate minerals that predominate in this layer; experiments have shown that, despite being heavier, iron droplets become trapped within the structure of the silicates, which would have prevented further movement downwards to the core. In 2013, a new theory was developed from tests on iron and silicates, which used a diamond anvil cell to simulate the temperature and pressure within the mantle. Three-dimensional imaging techniques showed what was happening at a molecular level. It was found that as the temperature and pressure increased, iron droplets trapped in the structure began to wet the surfaces of the silicate minerals, and this allowed the iron to slide through the structure and come together to form channels of liquid that percolated

Above: An early example of a diamond anvil cell, used to recreate the extreme pressure at the Earth's core.

downwards. If this has also happened in the mantle, it suggests that the formation of the core has been an ongoing process, rather than one that only occurred before the internal structure of the Earth formed. It may also help to explain the strength of the Earth's magnetic field compared to our neighbouring planets. As we will see in the following pages, this is generated in the outer core, and plays an important role in shielding the planet from the effects of solar wind and potentially harmful cosmic rays.

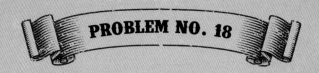

WHY DOES THE EARTH'S MAGNETIC FIELD REVERSE?

Field: Geology, geophysics
Location: From the outer core to the magnetosphere

One of the the properties of our planet that we have struggled to explain is the fact that its magnetic field occasionally reverses. If this happened today, it would mean that our compasses would point to the south, rather than to the north.

A reversal in the magnetic field is probably not something we need to get overly worried about because the last full one occurred 780,000 years ago, while a partial reversal, known as a geomagnetic excursion, last happened 41,000 years ago – when the poles reversed for a few hundred years before flipping back again. The generally accepted theory of how the Earth's magnetic field is generated states that heat from the solid inner core of the planet causes chaotic and swirling convection currents in the liquid outer core, and, as it is predominantly composed of magnetised iron, this rotational movement works like a giant dynamo, inducing a moving electric current, together with its accompanying magnetic field. The action of this geodynamo, as it is known, is thought to lead to the polarity of the planet and to maintain the magnetosphere, the region of space around the Earth to which the magnetic field extends.

The possibility of the magnetic field reversing was first proposed in 1906 by the French geologist Bernard Brunhes, after he had studied iron minerals in volcanic rocks from Auvergne, the region of central France well-known for its numerous extinct volcanoes. This was based on an anomaly he observed, in which some crystals of magnetic iron minerals in the volcanic rocks are orientated either to the north or south. Shortly afterwards, the Japanese geophysicist Motonori Matuyama carried out a systematic study of volcanic basalt rocks in different locations in Japan and China, which demonstrated that rocks in the same geological layers – ones that had been laid down at the same time – showed the same polarity, described as normal where iron minerals are oriented to the north, and reversed in those pointing south.

Matuyama's work provided clear evidence to support the theory that the poles had reversed in the past, but it did not receive any great attention until the 1950s, when radiometric methods of dating rocks based on the decay of radioactive isotopes were

Above: A view of the volcanic Massif Central in the Auvergne region of central France.

developed, which allowed a chronology to be worked out. The pioneers of the field were later recognised, with their names being assigned to the periods, known as chrons, of normal or reversed polarity. We are currently in the Brunhes Normal Chron, which began 780,000 years ago, and this was preceded by the Matuyama Reversed Chron, beginning 2.59 million years ago, while the period during which the flip took place is called the Brunhes–Matuyama Transition. It used to be thought that this flip occurred over the course of thousands of years, but recent research, published in 2014, suggests that it could have been much quicker, perhaps taking as little as 100 years.

Opposite: Gary Glatzmaier's and Paul Roberts's pioneering simulation of the Earth's magnetic field.

THE FLIPPING FIELD

We don't know what causes a reversal in polarity and may well have to wait until it happens again before we have the opportunity to study the phenomenon in enough detail to find

Below: An accelerator mass spectrometer, used to determine radiometric dates by analysing the radioactive decay of isotopes.

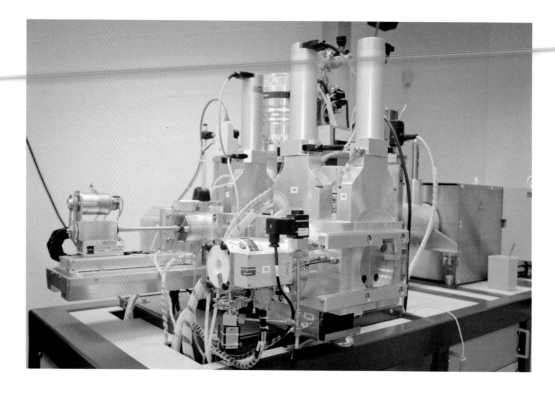

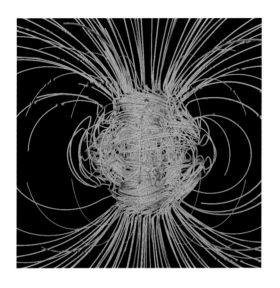

out. We currently lack a clear enough understanding of what is happening in the outer core and mantle to generate the magnetic field in the first place, let alone know why it flips. Past reversals have occurred over an apparently random time frame, so it is impossible to predict when the next one will be. A gradual weakening of the magnetic field recorded over the course of the last century has led to some speculation that we are entering a transitional period, but, as we don't know anything about the processes leading up to reversals, there is no way of knowing if this is really the case. A reversal may be beginning right at this moment, or it may not happen for hundreds of thousands of years.

One way of investigating reversals in the Earth's polarity is to construct computer models of the way in which the Earth's magnetic field is generated by the dynamo in the inner core, and then run simulations to see what happens. This involves attempting to recreate the interaction between the heat generated in the inner core and the convection currents thought to be the source of the magnetic field in the outer core, which, as we don't fully understand what is going on in either region, is extremely difficult. One simulation developed by Gary Glatzmaier and Paul Roberts at University College, Los Angeles in the 1990s uses a complex set of equations, involving thermodynamics and fluid motion, to describe the physical properties of the geodynamo. It was found to provide an accurate model for the generation of known variations in the magnetic field, and, when run to simulate the changes occurring in polarity over hundreds of thousands of years, showed the process of reversal occurring on a number of occasions. The timing of the reversals was random, and apparently caused by the development of a particular set of circumstances, in which the thermodynamics and fluid motion evolved with the generation of the magnetic field in such a way as to weaken the strength of the poles. If the strength of the poles dropped below a certain point, this caused a reversal.

THE IMPACT OF REVERSALS

If computer-generated models accurately simulate what is happening in the outer core, and reversals are indeed caused by a weakening in the magnetic field, then this has implications for the ability of the magnetosphere to deflect potentially harmful high-energy particles found in cosmic radiation. If the magnetic field were to disappear completely, the planet could also be exposed to solar wind. This is thought by some scientists to have occurred on Mars, which does not have a magnetic field, and thus any atmosphere that may have existed would have effectively blown away. Needless to say, this would be disastrous for our planet, but as there have been numerous reversals in the past and the Earth still has an atmosphere, it is reasonably safe to assume that this scenario is not very likely to happen here.

Studies of transitional periods that lead to reversals and their impact on life on Earth have actually found nothing to suggest any harmful effects. There is, for instance, no correlation between the timing of reversals and extinction events or periods of increased seismic and volcanic activity. So it would appear that, beyond the disruption it would cause to our navigational systems, and the possibility of interference with some communications, we don't have a great deal to worry about. There could be an impact on animals that make use of the magnetic field to navigate, though it would appear that reversals usually happen over the course of long enough periods to allow them to adapt. So in the unlikely event of a flip suddenly happening tomorrow, aircraft may have to be grounded while we work we out how to navigate, our phone services could be interrupted for a while, and homing pigeons might get rather confused. Other than that, we should be fine.

— ALTERNATIVE —
THEORIES

Above: Compasses point to the Magnetic North Pole rather than true north, possibly because of the Earth's lopsided inner core.

In recent years, seismic images of the Earth's inner core have been interpreted as showing it to be composed of slightly differing eastern and western hemispheres. One theory, known as translational instability, suggests that this difference is due to the growth of the core, caused by its cooling, being lopsided – with more iron crystallising out on the surface of the western side than on the eastern one.

In research published in 2012, Peter Olson and Renaud Deguen of Johns Hopkins University in Baltimore, Ohio, set out to test this theory, by modelling what would happen to the magnetic field if the inner core were lopsided. They found that the axis of the magnetic field in the model shifted to the side that was growing, which led them to speculate that this change in the axis in the inner core may cause irregular convection patterns in the outer core, which could be responsible for reversals in the magnetic field. They also thought that the position of the axis in the inner core could be the reason why magnetic north is not the same as true north – the Magnetic North Pole currently being off the coast of Canada, about 480 km (300 miles) from the Geographic North Pole. If this is correct, then tracing the movement of the Magnetic North Pole over time would give an indication of the way in which the inner core was growing, and perhaps would even show if a reversal in the magnetic field were likely to occur.

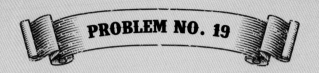

HOW DID TECTONIC PLATES FIRST FORM?

Field: Geology, plate tectonics
Location: The lithosphere

Our understanding of plate tectonics has come a long way since the theory of their existence was first proposed in the 1960s, but we still don't know how the plates were originally formed.

The theory of plate tectonics has had an enormous impact on geology, unifying its disparate strands and providing a solid foundation for the subject, in a similar way to evolution underpinning the biological sciences. The creation of continents and oceans, the rise of mountain ranges, the eruption of volcanoes and the occurrence of earthquakes, together with many of the other forces which have shaped the planet on which we live, can be explained by the movements of the mosaic of rocky plates that make up the surface of the Earth, as they slide over, under and past each other.

As important as the theory is, it is by no means set in stone. It evolves and adapts as new evidence comes to light, and there are a few glaring holes in our knowledge. Despite the illustrations in geology textbooks showing the plates moving either by being pushed along by convection currents from below, or dragged by

gravitational forces from above, in what is known as slab pull and ridge push, we don't know for certain exactly how these enormous sheets of rock move. And, at an even more fundamental level, we don't know how the plates on which the whole edifice of the theory rests were formed in the first place. As far as we know, the Earth is the only planet in the solar system which has tectonic plates, though it is thought possible that the surface of Mars is made up of plates that have stopped moving – so why is our planet so different from the others?

Above: A unique walkway in Iceland's Thingvellir National Park that runs between the North American and Eurasian tectonic plates.

MOVING PLATES

The plates are made up of the Earth's crust and the uppermost rocky layer of the mantle, together known as the lithosphere, which itself rests on the asthenosphere, a slightly more viscous layer of the mantle. The lithosphere is divided into two types: the oceanic crust under the sea, primarily composed of heavy gabbro

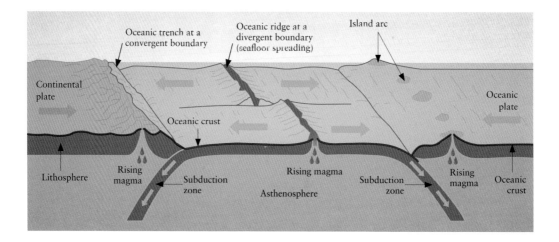

rocks, and the continental crust, made up of less dense granite, on which landmasses rest. The two different types exhibit different characteristics when plates come together. Where oceanic plates meet continental plates, for example, the heavier oceanic plate sinks under the lighter plate in a process known as subduction, forming a deep trench in the ocean, such as the one near the Mariana Islands in the Western Pacific. Where two continental plates collide with each other, the edges of both fracture and fold, as they are pushed upwards to form mountain ranges – a process that is currently happening as the Indian plate crashes into the Eurasian plate to form the Himalayas, which are still in the process of growing. Two oceanic plates moving apart, known as seafloor spreading, also results in the creation of mountain ranges (though these are underwater), because the gap that is opened up as the plates move becomes filled with magma welling up from the mantle below. The Mid-Atlantic Ridge is still being formed in this way, as the Eurasian and the North American plates diverge.

The boundaries between plates form some of the most geologically active regions in the world. This is particularly the case with the Ring of Fire, a horseshoe-shaped belt around the edge of the Pacific Ocean where volcanic eruptions and earthquakes are more

Above: A diagram showing plate tectonics, including seafloor spreading and the subduction that creates oceanic trenches.

Above: An aerial view of the San Andreas fault cutting across the Carrizo Plain in Central California.

common than anywhere else on the planet. One part of this belt is made up of the San Andreas fault, which runs down the coast of California, close to San Francisco and Los Angeles, and is where the northwestward-moving Pacific plate and southeastward-moving North American plate meet, resulting in numerous small earth tremours and sporadic full-scale earthquakes.

TECTONIC BEGINNINGS

The constant movement of the plates and the dynamic nature of their interactions make studying the early geology of the Earth difficult. The oceanic plates, for instance, are constantly being recycled by subduction, so that no parts of the lithosphere under the sea are more than 200 million years old – while the formation and breakup of continents, the rise of mountain ranges, volcanism, and the impact of erosion mean that the geological record of the early Earth above sea level is fragmentary. Investigating when and how the plates formed relies on ancient rocks found near the surface, and on computer models based on our knowledge of the Earth's early history.

Crystals of the silicate mineral zircon, found in the Jack Hills of Western Australia, have been dated as 4.4 billion years old, making this the oldest known material on Earth and an important resource in the study of its early geology. Zircons are very hard and durable, so they have endured while the rocks around them have disappeared over time. Traces of these surrounding rocks persist as impurities within the crystalline structure of some zircons, and research published in 2008 found the mineral muscovite inside some that were 4 billion years old. Muscovite typically forms today under the conditions found in subduction zones, and, though it may not have formed in the same way 4 billion years ago, it nevertheless suggests that tectonic plates may have formed by then, a much earlier period in the Earth's history than had previously been thought.

Subsequent research on flaws in 3-billion-year-old diamonds found traces of eclogite, a metamorphic rock formed when volcanic material from the surface of the Earth has been forced down into the mantle by subduction, where it is transformed under conditions of high temperature and pressure, before being returned to the surface again in volcanic eruptions. Eclogite can only be formed in this way, so its presence within the diamonds provides clear evidence that plates must have been moving by 3 billion years ago at the latest.

Above: The Tungurahua volcano erupting in Ecuador in 2011. Such activity brings material from the Earth's mantle to the surface.

One theory on how plate tectonics began combines the dates obtained in these two studies to suggest that subduction started 4 billion years ago and, over the course of the following billion years, this led to the formation of plates. Rocks that were subducted into the mantle melted and were pushed back to the surface by convection currents to form new sections of the lithosphere, creating weak spots that eventually cracked open to form separate plates. As subduction continued, the cracking spread over the entire surface of the Earth. What this theory does not explain is how the subduction could have occurred before plate tectonics got underway, but, despite its shortcomings, it does provide a working model of how plates may have formed.

— ALTERNATIVE —
THEORIES

Above: A 3.2-billion-year-old sample of rock from the Barberton greenstone belt in South Africa.

A different theory of how tectonic plates first formed suggests that cracks developed in the lithosphere after the Earth was hit by a large comet or asteroid. If the impact occurred at a point where the crust was relatively weak, a large meteorite could have smashed through the crust, opening up a crater all the way down to the mantle. The consequences of such an occurrence may have been to initiate an intense period of volcanic and seismic activity in which huge quantities of magma rose up from the mantle and spread out over the surface of the Earth.

According to the theory, cracks could then have opened up on either side of the crater and grown to form the boundaries of the plates. The continuing action of plate tectonics ensures that direct evidence of meteorite strikes from the early period of Earth's history no longer exists, and the earliest indirect evidence of a massive meteorite impact dates to 3.26 billion years ago, found in the Barberton greenstone belt in South Africa. Here, sedimentary rocks 3.6 to 3.2 billion years old have been preserved – some of the oldest in the world – including a layer containing much more iridium than usual, providing evidence of an impact event, though the actual location of the strike remains a mystery. The meteorite is estimated to have been between 37 and 58 km (23 and 36 miles) wide, which, if correct, would make it the largest one known to have hit our planet, and perhaps even one that played some part in the beginnings of plate tectonics.

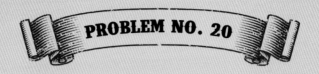
WILL WE EVER BE ABLE TO PREDICT EARTHQUAKES?

Field: Seismology
Location: In earthquake zones around the world

Earthquakes have been responsible for some of the greatest natural disasters in history, causing death and destruction on a vast scale. If we were able to predict these devastating events, the number of casualties could be dramatically reduced.

The theory of plate tectonics has revolutionised our understanding of earthquakes, allowing seismologists to describe how they occur and to identify those regions of the world most at risk. The vast majority occur along fault lines associated with plate boundaries, and are caused by a buildup of stress in the faults as the moving plates grind against each other. When the energy accumulated in the rocks on either side of the fault grows larger than the strength of those rocks to resist it, a slippage occurs, and some of the energy released radiates outwards, causing the ground to move and shake.

In the 1970s, it was thought that we would soon be able to predict earthquakes, giving people in the regions affected enough warning to at least take shelter, if not evacuate the area. Four decades later, the 9.0-magnitude earthquake that occurred on 11 March

2011, off the Pacific coast of Japan, illustrated that this has not been the case. Japan has the most sophisticated earthquake early warning system in the world and, when it was triggered in 2011, it provided at most a one-minute warning to urban areas. This warning relies on the radio signal used for its transmission travelling faster through air than pressure waves can move through rock, and it undoubtedly saved many lives. Even so, almost 16,000 people were killed, most of whom died as a consequence of the tsunami initiated by the quake – also the cause of a major incident at the Fukushima nuclear power station.

THE PARKFIELD EXPERIMENT
The 6.0-magnitude earthquake that occurred in the small town of Parkfield on 28 September 2004 had been predicted by seismologists. Parkfield is right on the San Andreas fault in Central California, and since the 1970s the town has been at the centre of some of the most intensive seismological studies ever to be carried out. In the 150 years leading up to 2004, six other earthquakes of

Below: The devastating impact of the tsunami caused by the 2011 earthquake off the Pacific coast of Japan.

similar magnitudes occurred around the town, and in 1985, after more than ten years of research, seismologists released a report stating that the next one would occur by 1993. The prediction was partly correct – the location was right, but the 11-year error in timing gives an indication of how difficult it is to predict an earthquake early enough for warnings to be given out.

What the seismologists in Parkfield and others around the world are hoping to find is some form of precursor to an earthquake that can be detected in the days and hours before it occurs, which can then be applied to earthquakes in general. Even if such a precursor were discovered, the procedure of giving out warnings would be a complicated one. Too many false alarms could lead to people ignoring the warnings and if, for instance, a warning was given out that led to the evacuation of Los Angeles or San Francisco but no earthquake actually occurred, the potential lawsuits against the government of California could be enormous.

Over the years, many different potential precursors have been suggested, but even though some have been observed before an earthquake, none have proved to be effective in predicting other earthquakes. Seismologists have monitored the buildup of stress in faults, in an attempt to discover if a particular type of sound wave or pressure wave can be detected immediately before rocks start to fracture, or if the buildup in stress causes an observable disturbance to the Earth's magnetic field. Another line of research, this time in Iceland, one of the most seismically active places on the planet, has investigated chemical changes in groundwater in the months before earthquakes have occurred, looking particularly at the concentrations of dissolved radon, a gas thought to be emitted as rock comes under stress.

So far nothing has come of any of these lines of research, mainly because the circumstances in which each earthquake occurs are different from any others: the structure of the rock and the

— ALTERNATIVE —
THEORIES

Numerous stories tell of some animals appearing to know when an earthquake is about to happen. Dogs are said to have become agitated in the hours before a quake struck and, after the 2004 Indian Ocean earthquake, stories emerged of elephants in Sri Lanka and domestic buffalo in Thailand both moving to higher ground before the tsunami arrived. Most seismologists dismiss these stories as myths, or as people attributing special qualities to otherwise normal behaviour with the benefit of hindsight. Those taking the phenomenon more seriously think animals could be reacting to high-frequency sounds emitted by rocks before a slip occurs, or those minor shock waves that travel through the ground more quickly than major ones.

Above: An elephant in Sri Lanka. Stories relate how animals moved to higher ground before the 2004 earthquake.

fault line are different, the nature of the stress it comes under is different, and the history of previous seismic events which may have weakened the rock is different. At the moment it is not at all clear these problems will be overcome, and, in the meantime, the best that can be done if you live in an earthquake zone is to be as prepared as possible.

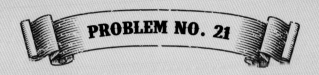

WHERE DID ALL THE WATER ON EARTH COME FROM?

Field: Hydrology, cosmology
Location: On our wet planet

The Earth is the only planet in the solar system to have expanses of open water on its surface, but, as strange as it may sound, we don't know where all this water came from in the first place.

The first astronauts to look down on Earth from space described it as being a blue ball and, looking at the photographs they took, it is easy to see why; more than 70 per cent of the surface of the planet shows up as the beautiful azure of the oceans. The wisps and swirls of white above the blue are, of course, clouds of water vapour – confirming that, though we may live on land, the Earth is in reality a water world.

One attempt to explain the presence of so much water on Earth suggests that it has always been here. If we go all the way back to the beginning of the universe, 13.8 billion years ago, the theory of the big bang states that huge quantities of hydrogen (the lightest element, consisting of a proton and an electron) were produced within the first few minutes after the explosion. Gravitational forces in the expanding universe brought some of the debris together to form stars, where nuclear fusion took

place, creating heavier elements, including oxygen. When these elements were thrown out into space as the stars eventually burnt out and collapsed, they formed clouds of dust and gas to add to the material from the big bang. Reactions between the elements in these clouds brought hydrogen and oxygen together to form H_2O, which is, of course, water. So when our solar system was formed about 4.6 billion years ago, as gravity pulled dust and gas together, water was an integral part of the process.

Above: 70 per cent of the surface of the beautiful blue ball on which we live is covered by water.

WATER FROM SPACE

Water, then, was present as the Earth formed, but the most widely held view on the earliest period of its history is that the planet was very hot and lacked an atmosphere, which would mean that any surface water would have evaporated off into space. One idea of how the Moon formed suggests that the Earth collided with an object about the size of Mars (with part of the resulting debris left orbiting the Earth), and that this massive impact, together with the numerous impacts of smaller meteorites during the Late Heavy Bombardment, ensured that surface temperatures stayed too high for liquid water to remain on the surface of the Earth for hundreds of millions of years. In these circumstances, it has been suggested that the water we find on Earth today arrived at some point after the planet had begun to cool and the atmosphere had formed, and was brought here by comets or asteroids. Some comets are known to be almost entirely composed of ice, though it would have taken thousands of impacts for the quantity of water found on Earth today to have accumulated in this way.

One of the findings of the European Space Agency's Rosetta mission, which landed a probe on the comet 67P/Churyumov–Gerasimenko in August 2014, was that water on the comet did not have the same chemical signature as water on Earth. It contained three times as much deuterium, an isotope of hydrogen that has a proton and a neutron in its nucleus – rather than the lone proton of normal hydrogen – and, when combined with oxygen, forms heavy water. This corresponds with observations from a number of other comets, so it appears unlikely that the water on Earth came from this source. Water on Vesta, one of the largest objects in the asteroid belt between Jupiter and Mars, appears to be more similar to water on Earth – so if it did not arrive on comets, it is possible that it came on meteorites that had split away from Vesta and other similar asteroids in the belt.

A different idea, based on studies of the same zircon crystals from Western Australia that we encountered when looking at plate tectonics (page 112), suggests that the Earth was not as hot and inhospitable during its early history as was previously thought, so that liquid water could have remained on its surface. If this were the case, it would have far-reaching consequences, because it would mean that the origins of life, the formation of the atmosphere and the beginnings of plate tectonics could all have

— ALTERNATIVE —
THEORIES

Above: A rough diamond formed in the Earth's mantle that could contain inclusions of such minerals as ringwoodite.

Research published in 2014 proposed that very large quantities of water, up to three times as much as in all the oceans put together, are present inside the Earth, in a transitional zone of rock about 700 km (440 miles) underground, between the upper and lower layers of the mantle. Traces of the water-bearing blue rock ringwoodite have been found within diamonds that were formed in the mantle, and seismograms also point towards the presence of the rock in the transitional zone. Experiments using a diamond anvil cell have shown that water is squeezed out of wet ringwoodite at the sort of high temperatures and pressure found in the mantle, and, if this also happened within the Earth, the water would most likely be forced upwards towards the surface.

occurred much earlier than is currently thought. The cool early Earth theory, as it is known, is not widely accepted at the moment, but, then again, the other theories about where all the water came from are not entirely satisfactory either. As wonderful as it is to have so much life-sustaining water on the planet today, we really don't know where it all came from.

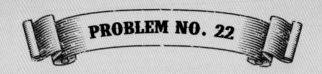

WHAT BROUGHT THE LAST ICE AGE TO AN END?

Field: Palaeoclimatology
Location: Around the North and South Poles

Research aimed at discovering the causes of past climate changes has increased in recent decades, because of what it can tell us about the climate today, and how it might change in the future.

The palaeoclimatologists among us, who study changes in past climates, reckon that we are currently living in the Holocene epoch, an interglacial period of the Quaternary ice age. An interglacial is a relatively warm period, when ice sheets have retreated from their maximum extent, but are nevertheless still present in the furthest northerly and southerly latitudes and will expand again once the climate cools down. 20,000 years ago, ice covered what is now New York City and most of the British Isles, stopping just short of where London is today. Slowly, the climate began to warm and the ice began to melt until, about 12,000 years ago, the ice had retreated sufficiently for most palaeoclimatologists to consider the last glacial period as having come to an end, though the dividing line between what constitutes glacial and interglacial is a fuzzy one. So, to rephrase the question posed here in a more scientific manner: what caused the climatic change that brought the last glacial period to an end?

MILANKOVITCH CYCLES

Scientific research into glaciation began in the 1830s with the work of the Swiss-American biologist Louis Agassiz, who studied how the glaciers of the Swiss Alps ebbed and flowed, and how this shaped the landscape over the course of time. In 1837, he proposed that, in the past, ice had once extended over a much greater area – a period he described as an ice age. One of the theories that attempted to explain how this had come about was developed in the 1860s by the self-taught Scottish scientist James Croll, who proposed that the ice age had been brought about by changes in temperature due to variations in the Earth's orbit and the influence such fluctuations had on amounts of sunlight reaching the planet.

Above: Louis Agassiz, the first scientist to propose that the Earth had experienced periods of glaciation, which he called ice ages.

Croll's theory predicted that there had been multiple ice ages brought on by the cyclical nature of the variations in the Earth's orbit, but it would not be until the 1930s that this was supported by firm evidence. This was provided by the Serbian scientist Milutin Milankovitch, who showed that changes in sunlight during the summer months in the northern hemisphere were a consequence of three different variations in the Earth's orbit – known as eccentricity, tilt and precession – and that, over the course of hundreds of thousands of years, these corresponded with the advance and retreat of ice sheets. Eccentricity describes the slight variations that occur in the Earth's elliptical orbit over cycles lasting 100,000 years, while tilt and precession involve changes to the way in which the planet spins on its axis. Tilt is the angle at which the Earth spins away from vertical, which varies between approximately 22 degrees and 24.5 degrees (it is roughly in the middle of these two at the moment) over a cycle of 41,000 years; and precession, which has a 22,000-year cycle, is the wobble the planet exhibits as it spins around its axis.

In 1976, corroboration of what are now known as Milankovitch cycles came when cores of deep-sea sediments were analysed and dated, providing a detailed portrait of how the climate has changed over the past 450,000 years. From the 1980s onwards, this time frame was extended backwards by a further 2 million years, through studying ice cores drilled out of Antarctica and the vast Greenland ice sheet. Atmospheric gases are trapped within this ice as it accumulates in seasonal cycles, and analysis of these gases has shown that the Milankovitch cycles are a major factor in climate change over the long term, though they do not fully account for all of the variations that have been observed. The cycles provide the background against which other, more short-term, factors influence the climate – chief among these being the

Opposite: Two scientists taking an ice core sample on Ross Island, Antarctica.

Below: Eccentricity, tilt and precession, the three variations in the Earth's orbit causing Milankovitch cycles.

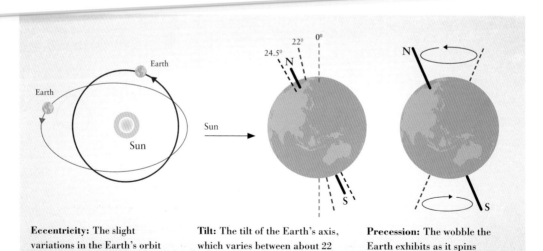

Eccentricity: The slight variations in the Earth's orbit around the Sun. Solar energy received by Earth is more varied when this orbit is elliptical.

Tilt: The tilt of the Earth's axis, which varies between about 22 degrees and 24.5 degrees. The poles receive more solar energy the greater the tilt.

Precession: The wobble the Earth exhibits as it spins around its axis. This affects the relationship between the planet's eccentricity and tilt.

level of carbon dioxide in the atmosphere, which has been shown to be one of the key driving forces behind past climate change.

THE STORY IN THE ICE

The analysis of ice cores allows us to reconstruct the climate change that led to the last ice age coming to an end. A relatively small increase in the amount of summer sunlight reaching the Earth about 20,000 years ago, as indicated by the Milankovitch cycles, led to northern ice sheets beginning to melt, increasing the amount of fresh water pouring into the northern oceans. This affected the currents circulating water between the northern and southern hemispheres, causing cooling in the north and warming in the south. As warm water can hold less dissolved carbon dioxide than cold water can, the warming in the south led to a release of the gas and a consequent rapid rise in temperature across the whole planet. More ice melted at both poles, again releasing large amounts of fresh water, causing sea levels to rise and further oscillations in ocean currents. Over the course of thousands of years, temperatures varied between warmer and cooler periods, while the accumulation of carbon dioxide in the atmosphere ensured that the general trend remained an increase in temperature. By about 10,000 years ago, the ice had retreated to expose vast areas of land in North America, northern Europe and Asia, and, with less meltwater entering the oceans, carbon dioxide stopped increasing and the temperature stabilised.

About 12,900 years ago, before temperatures stabilised, the northern hemisphere experienced a prolonged cold snap, known to climatologists as the Younger Dryas, which lasted for about 1,300 years. One theory suggests that people first began farming as a consequence of this sudden cold snap, through being forced to find alternative ways to provide food for themselves when the climate turned against them, though the sequence of events leading up to the adoption of agriculture is not entirely clear. Whatever the case, as the climate warmed after the Younger Dryas, farming began to spread out from its birthplace in the Fertile Crescent region of the Middle East, providing the basis for modern civilisation.

Our knowledge of how climate change brought about the end of the last ice age is now sufficient for us to have a reasonably good idea of the processes involved, but we should also recognise that it is far from complete, particularly in our understanding of the circulation of ocean currents. Another way of looking at it suggests that, in reality, the ice age never did end: we just happen to be living in a reasonably warm period at the moment, and, at some point in the future, the ice will return. Should that happen, New York and much of Britain could once again be covered in thick sheets of ice – a scenario that would make our current concerns over the impact of global warming appear insignificant by comparison.

— ALTERNATIVE —
THEORIES

The cold snap of the Younger Dryas may have come on very quickly, average temperatures apparently dropping by 10°C (18°F) over the course of a few decades. Climate change caused by natural variations in sunlight, brought on by Milankovitch cycles, is usually much more gradual, so palaeoclimatologists have attempted to find another explanation for such a sudden change. One theory suggests that the cooling was caused by an enormous quantity of fresh water being released into the Arctic Ocean from a giant lake in the middle of North America, which had formed as the continental ice sheet melted. Lake Agassiz, named after the Swiss-American biologist, stretched from the middle of the Canadian province of Manitoba in the north to Minnesota in the United States, and was considerably larger than all of the present-day Great Lakes of the region put together. As the ice sheet retreated further north, water from the lake flowed in a northeasterly direction, through what is today the Athabasca Valley and Mackenzie

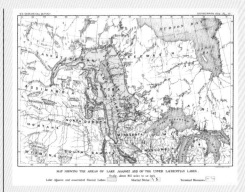

Above: An 1895 map by the US Geological Survey of the extent of Lake Agassiz, now thought to have been an underestimate.

River, until, about 13,000 years ago, it breached the remaining ice barrier, causing a massive outburst of floodwater into the Arctic Ocean. According to the theory, this sudden influx of fresh water interrupted the flow of warmer salt water coming up from the south (in what is known as the Earth's thermohaline circulation system), the knock-on effect of which was the period of intense and rapid cooling leading to the climate of the Younger Dryas.

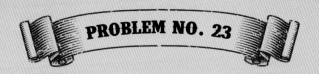

IS CLIMATE CHANGE A NATURAL PHENOMENON?

Field: Climatology
Location: Global

Over the last few decades, climate change has become a highly charged political issue, in which the science behind it often gets overshadowed. So, what does science actually tell us about what has been happening to the climate?

One thing we can say for certain about the climate of the Earth is that it has never been stable. The dynamic nature of the way it changes is currently the subject of vigorous debate and we still have much more to learn about this complex and often chaotic system. As we have already seen (see page 127), natural variations during the Milankovitch cycles and in the level of atmospheric carbon dioxide, together with other factors such as the circulation of ocean currents, can lead to major changes in the climate. At the same time, we are being told by climatologists that the warming we are experiencing today is primarily due to the amount of carbon dioxide and other greenhouse gases, such as methane and nitrous oxide, that we are emitting into the atmosphere by burning fossil fuels. Rather than being our fault, could this warming actually be the result of natural variations?

A WARMING WORLD

Almost every aspect of the science behind climate change has been disputed at one time or another – even the temperature records that show the extent of the warming that has occurred, shown to be about 0.8°C (1.4°F) since the beginning of the twentieth century. Records go back considerably further than this, but before about 1880 the measuring instruments were not very reliable, and recordings were only taken in a relatively small number of locations worldwide. The use of better technology, and an increase in the number of recordings taken by 1900, has meant that we can be reasonably confident that we are dealing with accurate information on how the climate has changed since that date.

In the early 1970s, the rate of warming increased noticeably, before beginning to level off over the past fifteen years – though this would appear to be the result of a particularly warm year in 1998 skewing the graph, rather than the warming trend actually coming to an end. Other indicators of temperature change also

Below: The view towards land, from a climate research vessel, of ice breaking up off the coast of Antarctica.

signal a warming trend, including a reduction in the amount of sea ice in the Arctic, the retreat of glaciers in many parts of the world, and a rise in sea levels – due to both warm water occupying a greater volume than cold water, and an increase in the flow of water from melting ice.

Since 1900, the level of carbon dioxide in the atmosphere has increased by 40 per cent, reaching 400 parts per million in 2015, a level that analysis of ice cores in Greenland shows is higher than it has been for over 2 million years. Burning fossil fuels (coal, oil and gas) releases carbon dioxide into the atmosphere and, after the start of the Industrial Revolution in the nineteenth century, atmospheric carbon dioxide increased gradually until the 1960s, after which it began to rise more rapidly as a consequence of the growing global population and increasing levels of affluence in the more developed regions of the world. One estimate puts the total amount of carbon released into the atmosphere through burning fossil fuels as half a trillion tons since 1850. While we don't know for certain exactly how much of the increase in atmospheric carbon dioxide comes directly from this source, it is difficult to pinpoint any natural variations that could account for the recorded rise in levels.

Above: Pollution from the Industrial Revolution in Britain, illustrated here by a shipyard on the River Clyde, Scotland.

NATURAL VARIATIONS

The Milankovitch cycles influence climate in a relatively gradual way over the course of thousands of years, and, in any case, according to what we know about how these work, the planet should be cooling very slightly at the moment, not warming up.

Above: A view of the Sun and the Earth across the solar arrays of the International Space Station.

As the water in the oceans warms, carbon dioxide is released, because warm water holds less gas than cold water does, but the immense volumes of water contained in the oceans mean that it would take hundreds of years before sufficient warming had occurred for significant amounts of carbon dioxide to be released.

One form of natural variability that has most likely contributed to global warming is that of solar activity. The Sun goes through a cycle of emitting higher and lower amounts of solar radiation over the course of eleven years, and this affects the amount of sunlight reaching the Earth's atmosphere. This has been measured by satellites since 1978, and since that time there has been no significant overall increase, beyond what can be expected as a result of the Sun's cycles. The UN's Intergovernmental Panel on Climate Change estimates that in the first half of the twentieth century, increases in solar activity accounted for 0.1°C (0.2°F) of the recorded temperature rise, but, since monitoring began, solar activity has not contributed any further rise. The Earth's atmosphere reflects about 30 per cent of incoming sunlight back into space, and this varies depending on factors such as the extent of cloud cover and the quantity of volcanic soot and ash in the upper atmosphere. Particles of air pollution known as aerosols, which are released by burning fossil fuels, also contribute to the amount of sunlight reflected, in a phenomenon known as global dimming, which, since the 1970s, is thought to have partially offset the warming caused by the release of carbon dioxide.

CLIMATE CHANGE AND US

The science, then, all points in the same direction – towards the likelihood that the principal driving force behind climate change since 1900 is the burning of ever-increasing quantities of fossil fuels. Other human activities thought to be responsible for about 25 per cent of the warming include large-scale deforestation and land clearance for agriculture. The IPCC estimates there is a 95 per cent chance the majority of climate change has been caused by human activities and, while this is an educated guess, it is most likely on the low side because, after coming under intense criticism in the past for overstating the impacts of climate change, the panel has become cautious in the announcements it now makes.

The complexity of the Earth's climate system means it is impossible to be certain about the impact of each component. The effects, for instance, of the changes in ocean currents in the South Pacific, known as the El Niño Southern Oscillation (more commonly El Niño and La Niña), are by no means fully understood, though it is clear it can have dramatic impacts on temperature and rainfall in many different regions of the world. But despite such gaps in our knowledge, it is clear enough that natural variation on its own is not enough to account for the warming, so perhaps the unresolved aspect here lies not so much in what is causing climate change but what we are going to do about it.

— ALTERNATIVE —
THEORIES

Above: Planting trees on its own may not solve the problem of climate change, but it won't do any harm either.

Over the past few decades, scientists have proposed numerous technological fixes for climate change, which involve either trying to prevent as much sunlight from reaching the Earth or removing large amounts of carbon dioxide from the atmosphere. Some of these are rather far-fetched, like erecting giant sunscreens in space, but others are more feasible. Large quantities of sulphur dioxide could be pumped into the upper atmosphere, which would have the effect of reflecting more sunlight, or iron filings could be added to the oceans, fertilising plankton that would then take up more carbon dioxide. No such schemes have yet been attempted because of the huge potential for unforeseen consequences, and because the sort of international agreements required are not likely to be possible.

An alternative strategy already exists that does not require any new technology or carry the likelihood of any negative impacts. All we need to do is plant more trees, which 'fix' carbon dioxide from the atmosphere and convert it into wood, providing us with a valuable and renewable resource, as well as a whole range of environmental benefits. However many trees we planted, though, reafforestation alone would not solve the problem of climate change. The only way to do that is to stop pumping out such large quantities of greenhouse gases into the atmosphere in the first place. But knowing what we should do and actually doing it are two very different things.

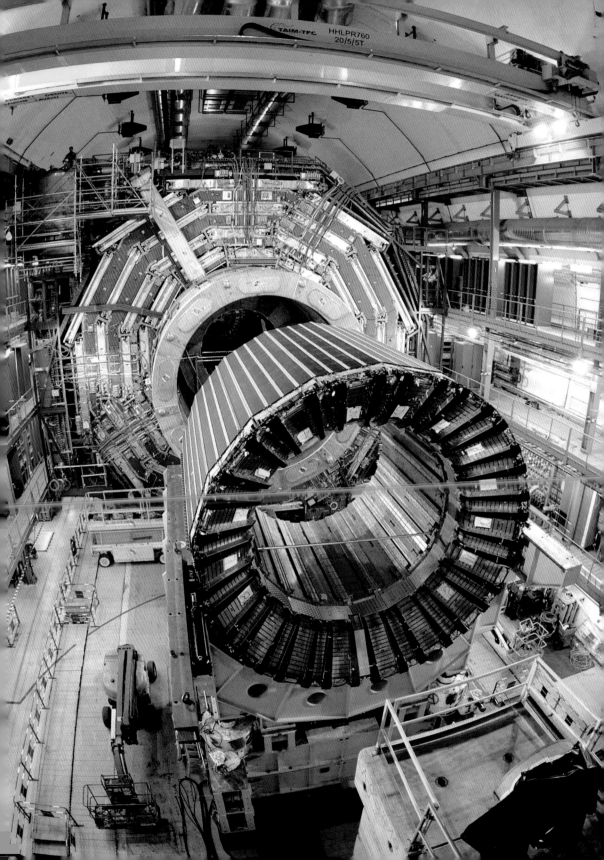

PHYSICAL SCIENCES

I t is hard to overstate the impact Albert Einstein's theories have had on physics since he first formulated them in the early twentieth century. A century later, his theory of general relativity remains one of the two central pillars of modern physics, along with quantum mechanics – and Einstein was involved in the early development of that as well. We begin by discussing whether light is a wave or a particle, an unresolved question that goes all the way back to Isaac Newton's day, and we also consider why there is so much more matter than antimatter, whether it is possible to exceed the speed of light, and why time only moves forwards. Then we take on the burning issue in physics today, discussing attempts to bring relativity and

quantum mechanics together in a quantum theory of gravity – an unsolved problem that perplexed Einstein, and for which an answer continues to elude us today.

Chemistry, it could be argued, has advanced rather more sedately than physics, though quantum mechanics is as much a part of chemistry as it is of physics. Here we look at the structure of water, which we still struggle to describe despite many years of research. We also discuss some practical applications of the physical sciences, including the potential for nuclear fusion to provide a clean source of energy, attempts to develop machines that can think, and the possibility of a quantum revolution in computing.

Left: The magnet core of the Large Hadron Collider at CERN in Switzerland, the largest experimental facility ever constructed.

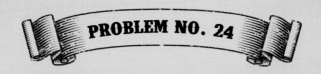

IS LIGHT A WAVE OR A PARTICLE?

Field: Optics, quantum mechanics
Location: Wherever there is light

The question posed here may appear straightforward enough, but trying to establish whether light consists of waves or particles has exercised some of the greatest minds in science.

I n 1905, a 26-year-old Albert Einstein was working as an examiner in the Swiss patent office in Bern, assessing the electric components of various new mechanical devices. Over the course of the year, he published four papers in the German scientific journal *Annalen der Physik*, and these, it could be argued, marked the beginning of modern physics, introducing the theory of relativity for the first time and making a major advance in the quantum theory that had been proposed by Max Planck five years previously. Einstein's *annus mirabilis* (miraculous year) was even more remarkable because, though he was writing a PhD thesis at the time, he was not formally attached to any academic institution, and beyond the electrical work he was doing at the patent office, the only help he received was through discussing his ideas with a group of like-minded friends in Bern.

WAVES AND PARTICLES

The first of Einstein's groundbreaking papers, and the one that concerns us here, proposed a theory to explain the photoelectric effect, the observation that light shining on a metal causes it to emit electrons. The prevailing wave theory of light, developed by the Scottish physicist James Clerk Maxwell in the 1860s, did not adequately account for this phenomenon – something that had only become apparent after the electron was discovered in the 1890s. Einstein's theory involved thinking of light as being composed of discrete packets, or quanta, with each packet containing sufficient energy to dislodge a single electron. He wrote that each of these packets was a quantum of light, later named a photon, and over the course of the twentieth century, this would develop into the idea of wave–particle duality as we understand it today, in which light is described as exhibiting the properties of both a wave and a particle.

Above: Albert Einstein, photographed in 1905, when the four papers he published revolutionised modern physics.

THE DOUBLE-SLIT EXPERIMENT

In some respects, Einstein's work harked back to the optical experiments conducted by Sir Isaac Newton in the 1660s, in which he shone a light source through a prism and showed that it was composed of the colours of the spectrum. From this, Newton developed the corpuscular theory of light, arguing that light was composed of particles that he called corpuscles – a view that was mostly accepted until the early nineteenth century. At this point, Thomas Young conducted his so-called double-slit experiment, which has become one of the most famous experiments in the history of science.

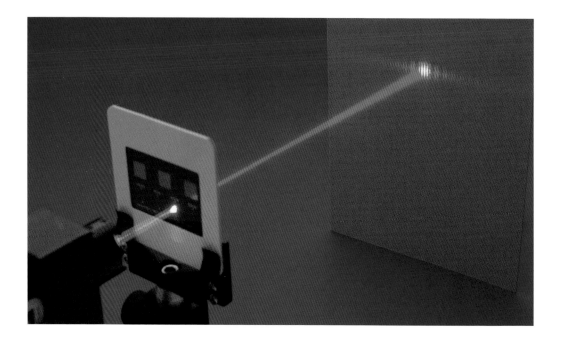

Right: The multiple bands produced on the screen by light passing through a double slit show that waves of light interfere with each other.

When light is shone through a card with two slits in it, instead of two bands of light being produced on a screen behind the card – as might be expected if light were made up of particles – a pattern comprised of multiple bands is actually produced. This shows that, as the light passes through the slits, it behaves like two waves interfering with each other, in the same way that waves produced in water affect each other when two objects are dropped in at the same time. The bands we see on the screen are the interference pattern produced by these two waves of light, in which the waves have either been amplified or cancelled out.

Young's experiment appeared to show that Newton had been wrong, and this was later supported by James Clerk Maxwell, who discovered that electromagnetic waves travelled at a constant speed, equal to the speed of light, from which he deduced that light must be a wave. Until Einstein came along, this appeared to have settled the debate, but after Einstein's theory was published, the quantum theory of light and wave–particle duality became

— ALTERNATIVE —
THEORIES

Fire a stream of electrons, rather than light, through a double slit and multiple bands will appear on the screen, showing these particles behaving like waves. If single electrons are fired through the slits one after another, we might expect to get two bands, but the same pattern of multiple bands appears again, as if the electrons have somehow remembered to carry on behaving like waves. Fit a detector to the experiment, which registers electrons passing through the slits, and something really strange starts to happen: two bands will now appear on the screen. Turn the detector off and the multiple bands return. This is an example of quantum weirdness, and anyone who manages to explain it

Above: In 2012, physicists at the University of Nebraska–Lincoln observed quantum interference in a notable example of the double-slit experiment.

can book an aeroplane ticket to Sweden, because a Nobel Prize will almost certainly be waiting there for them.

tenets of quantum mechanics, as developed in the 1920s by Niels Bohr and others. It is now widely accepted that the photon, along with other elementary particles, can sometimes behave as a wave and sometimes as a particle. Why this was so was once described by the American theoretical physicist Richard Feynman as being one of the central mysteries of quantum mechanics; it remains so today.

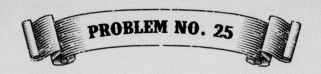

IS IT POSSIBLE TO DESCRIBE TURBULENCE?

Field: Fluid dynamics, mathematics
Location: In gases and liquids

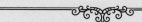

Anybody who has had a bumpy ride on an aeroplane has experienced turbulence, but those scientists who have attempted to describe exactly what is happening within a turbulent system have so far drawn a blank.

We know when we are experiencing turbulence in an aeroplane because the pilot tells us, no doubt attempting to reassure us as we spill cups of coffee in our laps, that there is nothing wrong with the plane itself. What has happened is that the plane has gone from smooth air to rough air. In fluid dynamics (physicists think of fluids as gases, as well as liquids) this is described as changing from laminar flow, in which the fluid particles are moving in streamlined, parallel layers, to turbulent flow, in which the particles are mixed together in a chaotic and unpredictable way. Much the same thing happens if you tip water out of a bottle at a shallow angle then increase that angle. At first the water flows smoothly as air rushes into the bottle and then, when the flow reaches a certain velocity, the water begins to glug out of the bottle as, in effect, it begins to struggle with the air coming in. Rather than flowing past each other, the air and water are mixing together, creating a chaotic system in which the movement of both has become erratic.

THE REYNOLDS NUMBER

The likelihood of turbulence occurring in the flow of a fluid through a pipe can be estimated by calculating the so-called Reynolds number, which is obtained by measuring the diameter of the pipe and the flow rate, divided by the viscosity of the fluid. The lower the Reynolds number, the smoother the flow, and, as a rule of thumb, if the number is below 2,000, the flow will be laminar, and the greater the number is above this, the greater the chance that turbulence will occur. It is a reasonably straightforward way of getting an idea of when turbulence is likely to occur, but does not take into account such variables as the friction within the pipe, which can cause eddies in the fluid, and lead to turbulence. It is more of a working solution to a problem, which gives a reasonably good guide rather than a definitive answer. It can also be extended to aerodynamics to give a drag coefficient, which attempts to take

Below: The aerodynamics of a US Navy seaplane being tested in 1932 at the Langley Full Scale Wind Tunnel, Virginia, USA.

into account the friction caused by air resistance as well. Rather than rely on these calculations completely, though, aircraft and car designers test how their new designs work in wind tunnels, to make sure that everything functions in the way it should.

NAVIER–STOKES

A fiendishly complicated set of equations concerning the motion of fluids was derived in the first half of the nineteenth century by the mathematicians Claude-Louis Navier and Sir George Stokes, which appears to give a more complete description of turbulence and, in simplified form, is also used in aerodynamic design. The problem with the Navier–Stokes equations is that they have so far resisted all attempts to be solved, so it is impossible to know for sure how closely they describe turbulence. In 2000, the Clay Mathematics Institute recognised the potential importance of finding these proofs by including the so-called Navier–Stokes existence and smoothness problem as one of its seven Millennium Prize Problems, offering one million dollars to anybody who could provide the solutions. This is essentially a problem of theoretical mathematics and it is not yet clear that a solution is even possible, let alone achievable. But should somebody actually manage to solve it and win the prize, the chances are that we will be able to gain a better understanding of turbulence as well.

A story that may or may not be true is told about the German physicist Werner Heisenberg, and illustrates the difficulties that surround an understanding of turbulence. Heisenberg worked with Niels Bohr in the 1920s in Copenhagen on developing quantum mechanics, and is now best known for the uncertainty principle named after him and for leading German efforts to develop a nuclear bomb during the Second World War. Before joining Bohr's research team in Copenhagen, he had written his PhD thesis on fluid dynamics, specifically on an aspect of turbulent flow. The story goes that, shortly before he died, Heisenberg remarked that, when he met God, he would like to ask Him two questions, one

— ALTERNATIVE —
THEORIES

Commercial pilots try to avoid areas of turbulence associated with particular weather systems and, when this is not possible, they ask their passengers to take to their seats and put on their seat belts. On occasion, though, a plane will suddenly sink – passengers' stomachs with it – without any warning, when it goes through clear-air turbulence. CAT, or air pockets as they are sometimes called, is not caused by the weather, so it is not picked up on radar systems. It most often occurs at the boundaries of jet streams – currents of fast-moving air used by airlines to increase speed and reduce fuel consumption. It is more uncomfortable

Above: View from the cockpit of a commercial plane. CAT is not picked up by weather radar so is difficult to avoid.

than dangerous, though passengers who are standing up when it occurs have occasionally been hurt.

about relativity and the other about turbulence – and he thought he would only receive an answer to the first of these. It may not be a true story, but our understanding of quantum mechanics continues to move forward while the chaos of turbulence remains as opaque as ever.

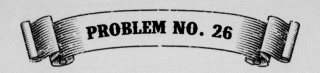

WHAT IS THE QUANTUM THEORY OF GRAVITY?

Field: Modern physics, relativity, quantum mechanics
Location: Everywhere and nowhere

A big hole currently exists at the heart of modern physics, as its two central pillars, relativity and quantum mechanics, are not compatible with each other – and it is not at all clear how these theories can be reconciled.

General relativity is a theory of gravity that explains what happens on a very large scale, with stars, galaxies and beyond. It was first articulated by Albert Einstein in 1915, building on his own special theory of relativity of 1905, which had contained the key insight that bodies of sufficiently large mass, such as stars, caused time to bend. This had led him to link space and time together, in the single interwoven concept of four-dimensional space–time (where time is the fourth dimension). He described the effect of large masses causing this space–time to curve, leading to time dilation – when time, instead of being constant, literally varies, like the other three dimensions of space (length, width and height). Over the next ten years, Einstein worked out equations to bring special relativity and Newton's law of gravity together, to create the general theory of relativity, which remains the accepted gravitational theory today.

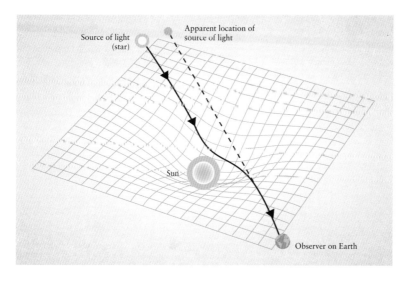

Source of light
(star)

Apparent location of
source of light

Sun

Observer on Earth

Left: A diagram showing
the effect of gravity
on the curvature of
space–time. In 1919 it
was shown that the Sun's
large mass causes light
from other stars to bend.

The first evidence in support of general relativity came in 1919,
arising from observations of a solar eclipse made by the British
astronomer Arthur Eddington. He showed that light coming
from stars that were observable during the eclipse, but were
otherwise obscured by sunlight, was bent by the mass of the Sun.
Einstein's theory had predicted that this would be the case, and
in the century that has elapsed since he first articulated it, almost
all of the other predictions he made have been backed up with
experimental evidence. The only exception is his prediction of
gravitational waves, which he described as being the ripples in
space–time that spread out due to changes in curvature as a large
mass accelerates. Even without the discovery of gravitational
waves, the weight of evidence backing up relativity means that it
is very unlikely to be incorrect – or, at least, if it is wrong then a
great deal of modern physics is also wrong.

INSIDE THE ATOM

Quantum mechanics emerged from the same roots as relativity –
the realisation that Newton's classical physics weren't enough to
explain the nature of all things. Though in this case, rather than
dealing with space–time and gravity, it concerns the very small:

atomic and subatomic particles. As we have already seen, Einstein
was involved in the beginnings of quantum theory (page 140),
but rather than being expressed as a single theory like relativity,
it developed in small steps over the course of the twentieth
century and is still evolving today. At heart, quantum mechanics
is a set of mathematical rules aimed at explaining what happens
inside an atom, where, according to the uncertainty principle,
it is impossible to determine both the position and velocity of a
particle at the same moment. Instead, we can only work out the
probability of a particle's location – a concept that led the sceptical
Einstein to remark that God does not play dice.

There is an even more impressive body of evidence supporting
quantum mechanics than there is for relativity, including the
construction of what is known as the Standard Model of particle
physics. Here, quantum theory predicted the existence of several
different types of elementary particles, which have since been

Opposite: A section of the 27-km (17-mile) long Large Hadron Collider at CERN in Switzerland.

confirmed by experiment. These have included various quarks and bosons – most recently the Higgs boson, predicted in the 1960s and provisionally confirmed in 2013, using the Large Hadron Collider at CERN in Switzerland. Quantum mechanics is also at the heart of the technology many of us use every day – the transistors and integrated circuits in our phones and computers – and was the theoretical basis for the development of nuclear fission. So, as these technologies all work, it appears to be inconceivable that the theory behind them is wrong.

THE THEORY OF EVERYTHING

General relativity and quantum mechanics, then, are different ways of resolving the shortcomings of classical physics, and, as far as the evidence goes, both appear to be correct. If this is the case, though, there must be a point at which the two come together. But in those few theoretical situations in which the two interact – where size is extremely small and mass very high, such as at the big bang and within black holes – the theories contradict each other. One explanation for this is that the universe is not a consistent place that can be described fully in terms of logically derived theories.

Below: Centaurus A, a galaxy thought to have a central black hole – where, in theory, general relativity and quantum mechanics interact.

Or, general relativity and quantum mechanics can be unified within a new theory that can account for both at the same time. Theoretical physicists are not keen on the first of these two options, which would mean they have been wasting their time, and are instead investigating ways of bringing the conflicting theories together as a quantum theory of gravity.

General relativity deals solely with gravity, while quantum mechanics is concerned with the three other fundamental forces of the universe:

the electromagnetic force, the strong nuclear force and the weak nuclear force. Each of these has an elementary particle associated with it – the photon, the gluon and the boson, respectively – so one approach to finding a quantum theory of gravity has been to propose a hypothetical particle for gravity, the graviton, and then try to prove that it exists, using quantum theory. Unfortunately for theoretical physics this approach has not so far proved fruitful, because the calculations based on the equations it has produced all lead to infinity, and no way of preventing this from happening has been found through what is known as renormalisation.

STRING THEORY

One way of attempting to overcome this problem has been through string theory, which takes as its starting point the concept that the universe is not made up of point-like particles, as envisaged in the Standard Model of particle physics, but is instead composed of vibrating strings, which, according to the theory at least, can produce elementary particles such as the graviton, depending on how they vibrate. In order to work, string theory requires the inclusion of numerous extra dimensions and elementary particles, making it extremely difficult to relate the theory to the observable world. Efforts to reduce this complexity have produced multiple offshoots, such as superstring theory and M-theory, but it is by no means clear whether any of these are actually leading towards a quantum theory of gravity or whether it is all just heading up a theoretical blind alley.

Proponents of string theory in its various different forms have described it as a way of constructing a quantum theory of gravity and of achieving the holy grail of theoretical physics – combining all four of the fundamental forces in a so-called theory of everything, which could explain all the physical processes in the universe from the big bang onwards. Quantum gravity, should we ever find it, could prove to be one step forward in the search for this ultimate theory, or it could actually be the entire theory itself.

— ALTERNATIVE —
THEORIES

Above: The theoretical physicist Carlo Rovelli, a principal proponent of loop quantum theory.

One of the criticisms of string theory has been that, whenever problems with the theory have arisen, solutions have been proposed which rely more on the imagination than on testable science. An alternative approach is loop quantum theory, which attempts to combine relativity and quantum mechanics using only those hypotheses that already exist within either of the two theories. At heart it is an attempt at the 'quantisation' of relativity, reasoning that, as quantum mechanics has shown us, matter is made of small packets of quanta – of electrons, photons and other particles. Rather than being continuous, space could also have a quantum structure. Here, space is envisaged as being granular, made up of incredibly small 'atoms of space', as they are described by Carlo Rovelli, the Italian theoretical physicist who has been one of the leading proponents of the theory. These grains are linked together in so-called loops, which form a structure described as a network in one version of the theory and a foam in another.

If the theory proves accurate, it should be possible to describe space using quantum mechanics, with a quantum theory of gravity. The next step is to provide experimental evidence of these loops and networks. Should this be achieved, it will represent a fundamental shift in our understanding of the universe and everything that is contained within it.

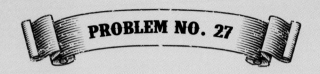

IS IT POSSIBLE TO EXCEED THE SPEED OF LIGHT?

Field: Relativity
Location: In a galaxy far, far away

According to the laws of physics, nothing should be able to go faster than the speed of light, which is a constant used in many theories, including Einstein's special theory of relativity.

In science-fiction books and films, exceeding the speed of light has become a routine plot device to get the protagonists from one place in the universe to another without disrupting the plot. Captain Kirk orders Lieutenant Sulu to go to warp speed and the *Enterprise* shoots off across the universe in a blur of starlight that hardly ruffles Spock's hairdo, while Han Solo and Chewbacca, with some help from R2-D2, pilot the *Millennium Falcon* into hyperspace and zip over to planets in faraway galaxies. Of course, enjoying *Star Trek* and *Star Wars* requires a certain suspension of disbelief, so bending the laws of physics is unlikely to cause great debates among fans on the inconsistencies between these journeys and Einstein's special theory of relativity – unless, that is, they really don't have anything else to do.

In reality, most physicists think that it is not possible to exceed the speed of light, which is, when measured in a vacuum, 299,000 km

(186,000 miles) per second – roughly a million times greater than the speed of sound. It takes just over eight minutes for sunlight to reach the Earth, while light from the second-nearest known star, Proxima Centauri, takes about four years to get here. The deep-field observations of the Hubble Space Telescope, which has been orbiting the Earth since 1990, have produced images of galaxies so far away that the light from them has taken more than 13 billion years to reach us – so not only are we able to look at incredibly distant stars, but also at ones that first formed relatively soon after the big bang and most likely ceased to exist billions of years ago.

MICHELSON–MORLEY

The development of Einstein's special theory of relativity was to some extent inspired by an experiment conducted in 1887 by the American physicists Albert Michelson and Edward Morley, who wanted to show that light moved through a medium in space called the ether, just as sound moves through air. The Michelson–Morley experiment attempted to demonstrate the presence of this

Left: The Hubble Space Telescope, which can observe distant galaxies without the distortion of the Earth's atmosphere.

ether, using the speed of light to detect the motion of the Earth at different times, as it was thought that the friction of the ether would cause the planet to move through it at varying speeds. They used two lights – one pointing in the direction the Earth was travelling and the other at a right angle to that – and attempted to detect the difference in the speed of light between the two, which could then be used to calculate the velocity of the Earth. As no difference could be detected at any time, the experiment failed to find the ether, instead providing evidence that it did not exist. But what it did suggest was that the speed of light remained constant in all circumstances, and that either distance or time must have varied. Since time was considered immutable, it was assumed that distance was the variable, until Einstein showed in the special theory of relativity that time could vary as well – as we have just seen in 'What is the quantum theory of gravity?' (page 148).

$E=MC^2$

In the last of the four papers Einstein published in 1905, he addressed one of the implications of special relativity, known as mass–energy equivalence. This showed that mass and energy can be related to each other, through the famous equation $E=mc^2$ – or, in plain words: energy equals mass multiplied by the speed of light, squared. The reason this equation has become so well-known is that it predicts the enormous energy that is held within very small particles such as atoms, which is what was released by the atomic bomb. It also shows why, according to the special theory of relativity, it is not possible to exceed the speed of light. For an accelerating object with mass – unlike the massless photons of light – as the velocity approaches the speed of light, the mass increases exponentially, so that the energy required to accelerate it further approaches infinity.

As mass increases, time slows down, and, in theory, would come to a stop at the speed of light, so, with time no longer running, velocity could not possibly increase any further. So before we fire

— ALTERNATIVE —
THEORIES

In the weird world of quantum mechanics, the strangest phenomenon of all must be entanglement, in which particles are linked in such a way that a change in one instantaneously impacts on the other, however far apart they happen to be. Einstein thought this idea was nonsense, describing it as 'spooky action at a distance', but it has since been backed up by experimental evidence. In 2011, for instance, researchers demonstrated the phenomenon occurring between photons 143 km (89 miles) apart, calculating that, if there was some form of communication between the particles, it moved at 10,000 times the speed of light – though they thought that it was more

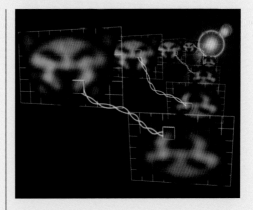

Above: A false-colour montage of actual quantum images obtained in a National Institue of Standards and Technology experiment, demonstrating quantum entanglement.

likely the result of a quantum property that we haven't quite figured out yet.

up the warp drive, we are going to have to work out a way of bypassing the special theory of relativity, or else Jim, Spock, Sulu and the rest of the crew of the *Enterprise* will be heading off into infinity rather than setting out on their next five-year mission.

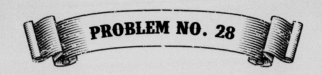

WHY DOES TIME ONLY MOVE FORWARDS?

Field: Thermodynamics, entropy, cosmology
Location: Everywhere, but only in one direction

In the laws of physics, from Newton to Einstein and beyond, there is nothing to suggest that time can only move in one direction – so why does it only go forwards?

The vast majority of us don't need the laws of physics to explain which direction time is going: we live in the present, what's done is done, and we don't know what the future may bring. Theoretical physicists, though, are a little different from the rest of us. They worry about the reasons for space having three dimensions while time only has one, and, as it doesn't matter to the laws of physics which way time is going, why does it only go in one direction? Rather than accepting that our world is just the way it is, they have attempted to find explanations, and one approach has been to link the arrow of time to entropy, another physical property that only has one direction.

In physics, entropy is concerned with thermodynamics, the way in which heat works. It is a measure of the amount of thermal energy in a system that is unavailable for conversion into mechanical work, which is one way of expressing the second law

of thermodynamics. What this means, put simply, is that over time things tend to fall apart, or, put yet another way, entropy always increases with time, so that systems increasingly become more disordered and chaotic. The first person to link the direction of time with entropy was the Austrian physicist Ludwig Boltzmann, who developed a theory in the 1870s that entropy increased because heat increased the motion of atoms, causing these particles to become more mixed up. At that time, many physicists did not accept the theory that matter was composed of atoms and molecules, proposed by the British chemist John Dalton more than 60 years previously, and it would not be until a few years after Boltzmann's death in 1906 that his theory of entropy would become widely accepted.

Above: The Austrian physicist Ludwig Boltzmann, whose theory of entropy would not be widely accepted until after his death.

THE DIRECTION OF THE UNIVERSE

Boltzmann's view of entropy was that everything in the universe is moving from a low state to a high one, because atoms are becoming more disordered. This is why, for instance, ice in a glass of water melts, or why a cup of coffee slowly cools down over time, and, since the entropy involved does not reverse on its own and is dependent on time, then time cannot be reversed either. An analogy often used to illustrate this is that, once an egg has been broken, it cannot then be unbroken, or, in other words, entropy and time go forward together, from the past to the future.

In Boltzmann's day, physicists considered the universe to be eternal and unchanging, so the suggestion that it was becoming more disorganised over time as entropy increased was not widely

Left: Time only moves in one direction, so, if you drop an egg, there is no going back.

accepted. This view of an unchanging universe became increasingly untenable (to physicists at least) after Einstein published the special theory of relativity in 1905, and even more so in the 1920s, when astronomers observed that galaxies are moving apart, leading them to conclude that the universe is not constant, but is expanding. This implies that by working backwards we can arrive at the beginning of the universe, which, as we will see in the next section, led to the theory of the big bang. This was based on Einstein's general theory of relativity and envisages that the universe began from a very small and very hot point, and, as it expanded, it cooled – in the process forming everything in existence. This is thought to imply that the universe is moving from very low to very high entropy so that, while it continues to expand, time will continue to move forwards, but if the expansion stops and the universe begins to contract, then time will go into reverse.

Needless to say, this is entirely theoretical at the moment, and in order to gain a better understanding of the relationship between time and the expanding universe, we need to be able to go right back to the big bang itself. General relativity leads us back to a point where the universe was infinitely small and of infinite mass, but at the moment we are not actually able to describe what

— ALTERNATIVE —
THEORIES

Of the four fundamental forces, gravity is the only one that acts in one direction, in that it is a force of attraction, while the electromagnetic force, strong nuclear force and weak nuclear force both pull and push. This has led to the idea that gravity and time are linked, and that in the early history of the universe, when gravity is thought to have been the dominating force, it somehow pulled a single arrow of time into pointing in one direction. Before that happened, according to the theory, there were many arrows pointing in all different directions – which, if that were the case today, would be a handy excuse for being late for work.

Above: This signpost shows we can move in many directions, to occupy different positions in physical space; the arrow of time only goes forwards.

happened at the birth of the universe. The hope is that a quantum theory of relativity, should we ever find one, will overcome this problem, and, in describing what happens at the beginning, we will also be able to describe the low entropy state of the universe – and, from there, understand why time moves forwards. In the meantime, if you drop an egg on the floor, don't expect it to unbreak itself. The universe hasn't stopped expanding just yet.

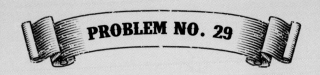

PROBLEM NO. 29

WHY IS THERE MORE MATTER THAN ANTIMATTER?

Field: Relativity, quantum mechanics, particle physics, statistical physics, cosmology
Location: Throughout the universe

According to theoretical physics, there should be equal amounts of matter and antimatter in the universe, but in actuality there is hardly any antimatter, and nobody knows why this is the case.

The concept of antimatter was first proposed in 1928 by the British physicist Paul Dirac, who was attempting to combine quantum mechanics with special relativity, and describe the properties of an electron. The results were unexpected: as well as describing the electron, his equation led to a theoretical particle with the same mass as the electron but with opposite properties when it came to charge and spin. From this, Dirac predicted the existence of the antielectron, or positron as it is now more commonly called, which has a positive charge, unlike the negative one of the electron, and spins in the opposite direction. Four years later, the American experimental physicist Carl Anderson discovered positrons present in cosmic rays, radiation from outside the solar system that is prevented from reaching the Earth's surface by the magnetic field and the atmosphere.

THE DIRAC EQUATION

The Dirac equation indicated that there should be equal numbers of electrons and positrons, and it has since become clear that every particle of matter should also have its equivalent particle of antimatter, so as well as electrons and positrons there are protons and antiprotons, quarks and antiquarks, and so on for all of the other particles. When the equivalent particles of matter and antimatter collide, they are said to be annihilated, effectively cancelling each other out and, in the process, releasing energy in the form of radiation. Antimatter can be made in particle accelerators, such as the Large Hadron Collider at CERN, in which two beams of particles can be accelerated almost to the speed of light, so that the particles collide with high energy – simulating conditions under which matter and antimatter are made in the universe and, it is thought, were made immediately after the big bang.

Above: The CMS experiment at the Large Hadron Collider, which aims to simulate conditions immediately after the big bang.

BARYOGENESIS

According to the Dirac equation and subsequent experimental work, equal quantities of matter and antimatter should have been produced after the big bang – but this can't have happened. This is lucky for us because, as matter and antimatter wipe each other out, if equal amounts of both had been produced, an enormous amount of radiation would have been produced in a big flash as the particles of matter and antimatter collided, and there would have been nothing left to form the universe.

As the universe does exist, something must have happened after the big bang to produce more matter than antimatter. Theoretical physicists have attempted to explain this phenomenon with what they call baryogenesis theories, after the composite subatomic baryon particle that accounts for almost all of the mass of atoms – and, by extension, almost all of the known matter in the universe.

One theory on baryon asymmetry – the universe's matter–antimatter imbalance – suggests that a flaw existed in the system that produced them, so a slight amount more matter than antimatter was made. Statistical analysis suggests this only had to be one extra part in a billion to account for enough matter being left over to form the universe – which implies that in total, the big bang actually produced enough matter for a billion universes, together with the corresponding quantity of antimatter, minus one.

One possible explanation is charge parity (CP) violation, a phenomenon discovered in 1964, for which the American physicists James Cronin and Val Fitch were awarded the Nobel Prize. They showed that under certain circumstances, particles called kaons and antikaons could decay at different rates, leaving a surplus of kaons. This surplus is far too small to account for the predominance of matter in the universe – being in the region f one part in a trillion – but it does establish the possibility of asymmetry between matter and antimatter. An ongoing experiment using the

— ALTERNATIVE —
THEORIES

Above: The Fermi Gamma-ray Space Telescope being prepared for launch at Cape Canaveral in May 2008.

Observations made in 2015 using NASA's Fermi Gamma-ray Space Telescope have been interpreted as showing giant magnetic spirals in space, which could be signs of CP violations. The theory goes that when matter and antimatter annihilated each other after the big bang, particles with a single pole were created for a fraction of a second and, if more matter than antimatter was produced, the resulting radiation will have left detectable magnetic fields, with left-handed spirals rather than right-handed ones. The magnetic fields detected were left-handed spirals, so if these were not formed in some other way, they could be signs of the CP violations necessary to produce the matter that forms the universe.

Large Hadron Collider, known as LHCb, has been attempting to discover CP violation in other particles and antiparticles, but we may have to wait for a clearer understanding of the big bang, as well as an explanation of dark matter (which we will get on to on page 196), before we finally get to the bottom of the mystery.

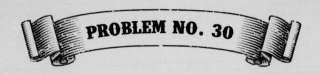

IS THE FUTURE OF COMPUTING A QUANTUM ONE?

Field: Quantum mechanics, computer science, information technology
Location: In a qubit

Over the past four decades, electronic devices using integrated circuits have steadily got smaller and faster, but a quantum revolution could be on the way, in which computing will become extremely small and very fast.

The integrated circuits, or silicon chips, in our devices work by allowing complicated but incredibly small electronic circuits to be built onto their surfaces. Information is stored in these circuits in what are called 'bits'. Each bit can have two values, usually represented by a 1 or a 0, and groups of bits can be used to represent more useful things, like letters of the alphabet, pictures or video. This information can then be processed by other parts of the circuitry according to yet more bits, which form the instructions of a program.

As the technology has advanced, an increasing number of transistors have been squeezed onto chips, from a few thousand in the early 1970s to 6 billion and counting today, but we are now approaching the limits of what it is physically possible to fit on a chip without a radical change in the technology used to build them. It is also becoming increasingly difficult to deal with the heat produced by billions of transistors switching on and off, and a further problem arises due to the individual components of the circuit having been reduced in size to that of tens of atoms, at which point the quantum phenomenon known as tunnelling makes it difficult to get a reliable current to flow in the wires.

QUANTUM SUPERPOSITION

A possible solution to this problem is to develop technology designed to work on an atomic scale, so that it can make use of quantum phenomena rather than be limited by them. One of these phenomena is quantum superposition, which allows particles with wave-like properties to exist in more than one state at the same time. This implies that, where a conventional bit can be either 1 or 0, a quantum bit, or qubit as it is known, has the probability of being either 1 or 0, so that it can be either or both when it is used. This may not sound all that impressive, but it means that the number of calculations grows by a factor of two for every

Below: An integrated circuit. We are now approaching the limit of what we can fit onto a silicon chip.

additional qubit. Two qubits can do four calculations at the same time, three cubits can do eight, four cubits can do sixteen, and this progression continues, so that before long the numbers get very large indeed. While a conventional computer plods along in binary, with each bit adding one more computation, the power of the quantum computer grows exponentially, so that, if the technology is available to harness this power, it becomes almost limitless.

MORE QUANTUM WEIRDNESS

The potential of quantum computing was recognised in the early 1980s by Richard Feynman and a number of other theoretical physicists, but transferring the idea from theory into a working model has proved to be immensely difficult, not least because scientists have had to find ways of dealing with quantum phenomena that are by no means fully understood.

If we take just the example of quantum tunnelling – which, as we have already seen, limits how small the components in conventional computing can be – some of the difficulties begin to become apparent. Tunnelling is a prediction made by quantum theory that there is a small probability of particles with wave-like properties being able to pass through a physical barrier without changing it. This has been confirmed experimentally, but we have no idea how this strange ghost-like property actually works, so designing a quantum computer that can utilise it, while not disrupting other quantum effects, is, to say the least, challenging.

Despite the difficulties, quantum computers are now beginning to emerge as commercial products, the first being made by the Canadian company D-Wave. These are about the size of a large wardrobe and cost millions of dollars, not least because the quantum effects they use require a low-noise environment, which is usually easier to achieve at an incredibly low temperature, approaching absolute zero. Numerous other research efforts are ongoing in an effort to find more practical hardware, as well as

ALTERNATIVE
THEORIES

A completely different approach to computing involves attempting to make use of DNA, the complex molecule that contains the genetic code of all living organisms. This code is in some ways comparable to the binary code of conventional computers, and advances in nanotechnology have enabled researchers to develop systems that can tap into it to perform calculations and store information. This can take minutes and hours rather than fractions of a second, so biological chips are not about to replace silicon ones. Nevertheless, researchers envisage a time when we will be able to program biological nanorobots to deliver the exact dosage of a drug directly into a cancer cell, killing it without affecting healthy cells.

Above: Attempts are being made to use the genetic code contained in DNA to produce groundbreaking biological computers.

develop the required software and, more generally, to assess what quantum computers could do better than conventional ones, which is most likely to be dealing with complex problems, where large quantities of information from many different sources need to be brought together. It may be some time before we are all using such machines, but experience would suggest that once a new technology gets going, it tends to snowball very quickly.

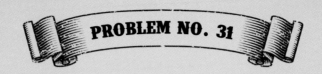

IS POWER FROM NUCLEAR FUSION POSSIBLE?

Field: Nuclear physics, chemistry
Location: Currently in the south of France, but potentially all round the world

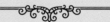

Nuclear fusion has the potential to provide an almost limitless supply of clean energy, but it is by no means straightforward, as it involves harnessing the same reaction that powers the Sun.

The nuclear power stations operating today, of which there are about 450 worldwide, make use of the energy released during nuclear fission to generate power. Fission involves bombarding the nuclei of a heavy element with neutrons (subatomic particles that are one of the constituents of the nucleus), which can split the nuclei and start a chain reaction. When a nucleus is split in this way, new nuclei are formed that have slightly less mass than the original one and, in accordance with Einstein's equation $E=mc^2$, a huge amount of energy is released in the form of heat, which in most nuclear power stations is harnessed to produce steam, used to drive turbines.

The problem with this form of power generation is that only the heaviest elements, uranium and plutonium, are fissile, which means these can be split to sustain a chain reaction. Both are

radioactive and, when the nuclei are split, the resulting waste is even more highly radioactive and can remain extremely dangerous for thousands of years. The accidents at the nuclear plants in Chernobyl and Fukushima illustrate the potential for disaster when something goes wrong, and, even when plants are working normally, we still have the issue of disposing of radioactive waste.

Above: A classroom in the city of Pripyat, Ukraine, abandoned after the Chernobyl nuclear accident in 1986.

FISSION AND FUSION

Nuclear fusion involves pushing two nuclei together rather than splitting one apart, and works best with hydrogen, the lightest element, instead of the heaviest ones. It takes place within the Sun, where huge gravitational pressure and temperatures of 15 million degrees Celsius (27 million degrees Fahrenheit) create conditions in which atoms of hydrogen break down into nuclei and electrons, to form what is known as plasma. The pressure forces two hydrogen nuclei to fuse, creating the nucleus of one helium atom with a slightly lower mass. So, again, a large amount of energy is released.

Nuclear fusion has been studied since the early 1950s, when the technology was used to produce the thermonuclear bomb. This uses an initial fission reaction to create the conditions for a series of fusion reactions to occur, unlike the earlier atomic bombs, which used fission alone. The potential of using the energy produced by fusion has always been apparent enough, but controlling it to generate power is by no means easy.

SOMETHING LIKE THE SUN

The main problem with fusion is that nuclei carry a positive charge, so they tend to repel each other. The conditions within the Sun are so extreme they overcome this repulsion, but recreating these conditions on Earth is a serious technological challenge. The gravitational pressure leading to plasma production within the Sun is about ten million times greater than the atmospheric pressure here, so, as it's impossible to get anywhere near that level, the temperature has to be much higher than within the Sun to compensate – about 150 million degrees Celsius (270 million degrees Fahrenheit) – before a plasma is created and fusion occurs.

While it is possible to achieve this enormous temperature, no fusion experiments have so far been able to reach the break-even point, beyond which more energy is generated than is used up. A further difficulty that has had to be overcome is known as confinement, which involves preventing hot plasma from touching

Opposite: The vast power of fusion was illustrated by thermonuclear bomb tests carried out in the 1950s.

anything, because there is no known material that could withstand such intense heat. The solution most commonly employed is to use a so-called tokamak, which was originally developed in the Soviet Union in the 1960s, the name deriving from the Russian words for its shape and function. Toroidal in shape, which means that it looks like a large ring doughnut, it uses powerful magnetic fields to heat up the fuel and hold the resulting hot plasma away from the solid surfaces on the tokamak's inside. A tokamak also keeps the plasma hot long enough for fusion to take place, so that the energy generated can be transferred from the fusion chamber and used to heat water for steam turbines to generate electricity.

The fusion reaction produces helium, an inert gas that is non-toxic and has no greenhouse effect when released into the atmosphere. Most attempts at developing a fusion reactor use two types, or isotopes, of hydrogen (called deuterium and tritium) because these give the most efficient reaction, producing the most energy at the lowest temperatures. However, this does result in a small amount

Below: The interior of a tokamak, where powerful magnetic fields hold hot plasma away from the inside surfaces.

of radioactivity, though at a much lower level than that from fission reactions and nothing like as long-lasting. Despite these few concerns over nuclear fusion, if fine-tuned on a large scale, it could potentially end our reliance on fossil fuels.

ITER

The cost of researching nuclear fusion is enormous, and though a number of countries are pursuing their own projects, the largest effort is a collaboration between the European Union, the United States, China, India, Japan, Russia and South Korea. It is known as ITER (International Thermonuclear Experimental Reactor; also a word in Latin meaning 'the way', providing the project's motto: 'the way to new energy'). The project has built on previous research, and is currently constructing a fusion reactor at the Cadarache nuclear power research facility in the south of France.

ITER uses the tokamak technology to heat and hold a plasma containing deuterium and tritium nuclei, the intention being to produce enough energy to exceed the break-even point by 2020, after which the target is to produce ten times as much electricity as is used. Deuterium can be extracted from seawater, so is readily available, but tritium is unstable and rare, though it can be made by bombarding the metallic element lithium with neutrons. The plan is to incorporate the production of tritium within the design, using the neutrons produced during fusion to create what is known as a breeder reactor that makes its own fuel.

If the project is successful, the next step will be to build a full-scale demonstration power plant, to be called DEMO, which it is hoped will become operational in the mid-2030s, providing a model for future commercial fusion power stations. ITER is currently a few years behind schedule and is likely to cost a great deal more than originally budgeted. But, should it succeed, it could lead to large amounts of energy generation at a very low environmental cost.

— ALTERNATIVE —
THEORIES

Above: Martin Fleischmann (left) and Stanley Pons demonstrating their work on cold fusion.

In March 1989, a press conference held by the chemists Stanley Pons and Martin Fleischmann at the University of Utah caused a sensation in the scientific community and in the mainstream media. Shortly afterwards, they published a paper giving more details of their work. They claimed to have constructed an electrolytic cell using a cathode made of the metallic element palladium, placed in a flask of deuterium oxide (heavy water), which led to a significant rise in temperature that could not have been caused by the power input or by a chemical reaction. One of the properties of palladium is that it can absorb hydrogen and deuterium, leading Pons and Fleischmann to interpret their results as showing that nuclei of the deuterium, released as a gas during electrolysis, had been squeezed together within the structure of the palladium, causing them to fuse and release energy. They had, they claimed, produced nuclear fusion at little more than room temperature – an extraordinary achievement when compared to the incredibly high temperatures used in hot fusion. Extensive tests were carried out in universities around the world but the results of the experiment could not be reproduced and Pons and Fleischmann, and their work, were publicly denounced by other scientists. If cold fusion really had occurred in a beaker of water, there would be no need to spend enormous amounts of money on ITER. But unfortunately it appears to have been a case of experimental error combined with a large dose of wishful thinking.

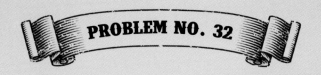

CAN WE MAKE A MACHINE THAT THINKS LIKE WE DO?

Field: Artificial intelligence, computer science
Location: Nowhere, at the moment

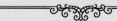

Research in the field of artificial intelligence, combined with advancing computer technology, means the prospect of making machines that think gets ever closer.

In May 1997, the IBM supercomputer Deep Blue beat the reigning world chess champion Garry Kasparov in a chess match played over six games, the first time a computer had achieved such a feat. The match attracted a great deal of media attention and, after Deep Blue had won, some journalists got carried away, suggesting that it was the beginning of the end for humanity. Kasparov, who acknowledges that he has never been a particularly good loser, saw things rather differently. He claimed that the IBM team had cheated by intervening in what the computer was doing, pointing specifically to a move it had made in the second game, which Kasparov had lost. The move, according to Kasparov, demonstrated a strategic sense of how the rest of the game would play out, which a computer should not be capable of holding, no matter how powerful it is, because computers work by making separate calculations for each move. In other words, the computer had thought like a human being, not like a machine.

Deep Blue applied the brute force approach to solving the problem of playing chess. It was powerful enough to make sufficient calculations per second to overcome our ability to think ahead and plan – assuming, that is, it really did beat Kasparov fairly. Up until then, the ability of computers to play chess was often used as a benchmark of how the technology was progressing, going right back to the beginnings of modern computing. In 1948, for instance, Alan Turing, sometimes described as the father of computer science and artificial intelligence, began to write one of the first computer chess programs, at a time when there were no computers fast enough to run it, forcing him to work out the calculations for each move on a piece of paper.

Above: Garry Kasparov (left) holds his head in his hands as an IBM scientist makes a move for Deep Blue.

THE TURING TEST

In 1950, the same year he completed his chess program, Turing published a paper in the journal *Mind* that is now regarded as a landmark in the development of artificial intelligence. In 'Computing Machinery and Intelligence', he addressed the central question of artificial intelligence: can a machine think? After defining what he meant by 'machine' and 'think', Turing presented an argument to show that it is possible for digital computers to be intelligent, starting a debate that continues today. In the same piece he also proposed an informal test to identify intelligence in a machine, which involved a computer in one room being able to convince people in a different room, asking it questions in writing, that it was human. A number of different versions of the Turing test now exist based on this theme, and occasionally a computer will pass the criteria, though so far this has involved its programmers adopting a strategy that tricks the questioners into believing they are communicating with another person, rather than the computer actually using language as we do.

The Turing test can, at times, be taken much more seriously than was originally intended – not least with those working on developing artificial intelligence. Turing regarded the test as a game that provoked people to consider what machine intelligence actually is and what its implications could be, rather than a way of confirming a particular computer has the same faculties as us. To achieve such faculties, a computer would have to exhibit general intelligence rather than the ability to mimic the way we think, which involves not only language but also the capacity to learn, to make decisions and plans, to solve problems by reasoning rather than brute force – together with all the other faculties we possess, as well as an ability to assimilate these together.

STRONG AI

This sort of artificial intelligence is sometimes known as strong AI, and can be contrasted with weak AI, in which a computer program has been designed specifically to emulate one facet of human behaviour. The computers designed to pass the Turing test are demonstrating weak AI, but there are currently no machines exhibiting anything approaching strong AI, and there is no prospect of their doing so in the immediate future. It is nevertheless worth questioning whether a machine with general

— ALTERNATIVE — THEORIES

Above: John Searle, who developed the so-called Chinese Room thought experiment.

The philosopher John Searle proposed a thought experiment, based on the Turing test, to challenge strong AI. Searle envisaged a situation in which a computer passes the Turing test, using Chinese characters to convince Chinese speakers that it is human. In a separate room, a non-Chinese speaker, such as himself, is provided with the instructions contained in the computer program (in English) and then receives the same questions (in Chinese characters) as the computer received. Given enough time, Searle argued, he could work through the instructions to produce the same answers in Chinese, showing that both he and the computer did not understand the questions or answers, but were simply capable of following a set of instructions.

intelligence could even be thought of as self-aware by humans; we struggle to explain our own consciousness, so it is difficult to know how we could explain what that would entail in a machine.

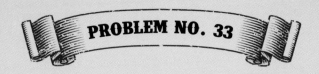
WHAT IS THE STRUCTURE OF WATER?

Field: Chemistry
Location: Wherever it is wet

If water were not as familiar, we would think it a very strange substance. It has a wide range of unusual properties and a structure that we still don't fully understand.

At its most basic level, the structure of water could hardly be much simpler. It is, as we all know, H_2O – two atoms of hydrogen bonded to one atom of oxygen. But as soon as we begin to investigate in a little more depth, some slightly unusual properties begin to emerge as a consequence of this apparently simple molecular structure, and the further we go, the stranger it gets. Professor Martin Chaplin of London South Bank University has compiled a list of 73 of these anomalies, some of which can be explained by what we know about the structure of water, while others are still mysteries.

One of the easier anomalies to explain is that ice floats on water, which we all know because when we put ice cubes in our drinks, they bob around at the top rather than sinking to the bottom. This happens because ice is not as dense as water in its liquid form. Water is one of the very few substances, and the only commonly

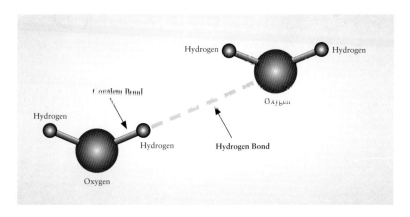

Left: The structure of water, showing strong covalent bonds between atoms and weaker hydrogen bonds between molecules.

occurring one, in which the solid is lighter than the liquid. When the liquid of other substances begins to freeze, the atoms or molecules slow down from the relatively excited state they were in, and begin to form the crystalline structure of a solid, in which the particles are held more closely together, making the solid heavier. The opposite occurs in water because of the structure of its molecules, which leads to the phenomenon of hydrogen bonding.

THE STRANGENESS OF WATER

The basic structure of water is V-shaped, with a large atom of oxygen at the bottom, and two smaller hydrogen atoms at the top that are attached to it by strong covalent bonds. The larger oxygen atom has a slightly higher negative charge than both hydrogen atoms combined, leading to the molecule as a whole exhibiting polarity, in which the oxygen atom has a negative charge and the hydrogen atoms are positive. These charges are quite small, but nevertheless the opposite poles attract between different water molecules to form so-called hydrogen bonds, which are much weaker than covalent bonds but still have an influence on the structure. As the liquid cools and less thermal energy is available, the molecules begin to move more slowly and get closer to each other, as in other substances – but then water reaches its maximum density at about 4°C (39°F) and, as it gets colder, the hydrogen bonds that form between the molecules effectively push them further apart, so that, as ice forms, it has a more open structure, occupying a greater volume of space. In cold conditions, this means ice forms on top of the water in lakes and rivers, leaving free-flowing water below in which life can continue to exist.

STICKY WATER

Hydrogen bonding means water molecules tend to stick together more than those of other substances, and this explains some of the other strange properties of water. It has

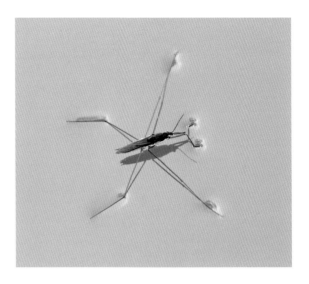

Above: A pond skater demonstrating the high surface tension of water by walking on it.

relatively high melting and boiling points, which means that it can exist as ice, water and steam within the relatively narrow temperature range on the surface of the Earth, allowing the natural water cycle to function. It has a high surface tension – as can be seen in those wildlife documentaries showing close-up shots of insects running across water, its surface bending beneath them – and this is also why capillary action occurs, in which water can flow upwards through narrow tubes, against the force of gravity. Then there is the capacity of water to absorb relatively large amounts of heat and, through the vast amounts of it on the surface of the Earth, moderate the climate.

These are just a few of the unusual properties of water arising as a consequence of its structure, which we can accurately describe in the gas and the solid but which has yet to be firmly established in the liquid. In water vapour, the molecules are free-moving, and in ice, hydrogen bonding leads to a structure based on four molecules forming a tetrahedron, which is like a pyramid with a triangular base, rather than a square one. In textbooks, the structure of the liquid is often also described as being composed of tetrahedrons, though these are described as being further apart than in ice,

— ALTERNATIVE — THEORIES

In 2004, water researchers were shaken up by a collaborative research project that included Anders Nilsson at Stanford University and Lars Pettersson of Stockholm University. Using the results obtained from a technique called X-ray absorption spectroscopy, they proposed that molecules in liquid water were primarily arranged in chains and rings, rather than the conventional tetrahedrons, and that this better explained its properties. The theory proved controversial, and has since been modified to include a small number of tetrahedrons. Subsequent research suggests that water may fluctuate between these different structures. However, no consensus on the subject currently exists.

Above: Droplets creating ripples on the surface of water may look familiar, but the structure of liquid water remains elusive.

with free molecules in the gaps between them accounting for the increase in density. Research has shown that this structure cannot fully explain all of water's properties and, as yet, no single theory has been able to account for everything. So, however familiar it may be, water remains a mystery to us.

ASTRONOMY AND COSMOLOGY

We have always been fascinated by the stars and the vastness of space, our curiosity leading us to observe what is happening up above and attempt to explain it. Astronomers are the ones who do the surveying and describing, while cosmologists think about what it all means – though the boundary between the two is not always a very sharp line. In the beginning, according to cosmologists, was the big bang, the name we have given to the most widely accepted theory of the origin of the universe. But even though we can describe what happened in the first few slivers of a second after it occurred, we have yet to uncover exactly what took place at that moment itself.

After considering the big bang, we discuss the controversial idea that there is more than just one universe, and the thorny subject of what the universe we do know is actually made up of. At the moment we can only account for about five per cent of its mass, while everything else is labelled dark matter and dark energy, because we can't see it and don't know what it is. From there we consider some of the more esoteric aspects of the universe, discussing what is inside a black hole, whether it will ever be possible to time-travel, and whether or not there may be extraterrestrial life. Finally, we reach the end by mulling over what cosmologists think will be the ultimate fate of the universe. Will it be a big bounce, a big crunch or a big rip? We really don't know, but there are scientists out there trying to figure it out.

Left: 'Pillars of Creation', a photograph from the Hubble Space Telescope of clouds of gas and dust in the Eagle Nebula.

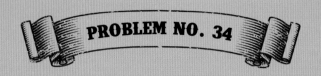

PROBLEM NO. 34

WHAT HAPPENED AT THE MOMENT OF THE BIG BANG?

Field: Cosmology, astronomy, theoretical physics
Location: At the beginning of the universe

The theory of the big bang is by far the best explanation we have of how the universe began, but we cannot describe exactly what occurred at the precise moment it happened.

The big bang theory states that the universe began as a tiny dot that was incredibly hot and dense, and that it has been expanding ever since. This idea was first proposed in 1927 by the Belgian priest and astronomer Georges Lemaître, who suggested that, in an expanding universe, Einstein's general theory of relativity made it possible to trace the origin of the universe back to a single point. Since that time what has become known as the big bang has been backed up by an impressive amount of evidence, so that now it is the most widely accepted account.

Two years after Lemaître had published his theory, Edwin Hubble came to a similar conclusion from his observations of red shift occurring in distant galaxies – a phenomenon caused by the Doppler effect, in which light shifts towards the red end of the spectrum when emitted from objects moving away from the observer. Hubble showed that this was caused by the expansion

of the universe and, though much the same as Lemaître's work, this observation has become known as Hubble's law. It provided further evidence that the beginning of the universe could be traced back to a particular point, but over the course of the next four decades this was only one of a number of competing theories. Its principal rival was the steady-state theory, championed by Fred Hoyle, Hermann Bondi and Thomas Gold at the University of Cambridge in the late 1940s, which described the expanding universe as being unchanging, with no beginning or end, and, in order for the density to stay the same as it expanded, it envisaged matter being constantly created. Hoyle was a vocal opponent of the other main theory, but inadvertently provided it with a name when he dismissively referred to it as 'the big bang' in a radio interview.

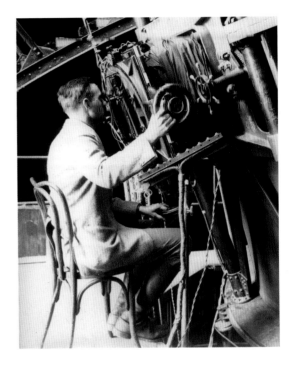

Above: Edwin Hubble, using the Hooker telescope at the Mount Wilson Observatory in Pasadena, California, USA.

THE COSMIC MICROWAVE BACKGROUND

At about the same time as the steady-state theory was being developed, three American cosmologists advocating the big bang theory – George Gamow, Ralph Alpher and Robert Herman – predicted that when the universe had cooled sufficiently after the big bang for the first atoms to form, radiation would have been released, which should still be detectable now. This cosmic microwave background, often referred to as the afterglow of the big bang, would provide convincing evidence in support of the theory, and, in 1965, the astronomers Arno Penzias and Robert Wilson announced that they had stumbled across it while using a Bell Labs radio telescope in Holmdel, New Jersey, to conduct unconnected research into satellite communications.

The discovery of the cosmic microwave background has been described by Stephen Hawking as the final nail in the coffin for the steady-state theory. Since this breakthrough, it has been used to research the early stages of the big bang and to map the observable universe in more detail than was previously possible, through using microwave telescopes on space probes. The rate of expansion of the universe derived from the cosmic microwave background has also provided us with a more accurate measure of the age of the universe – showing that it is 13.8 billion years old. When these lines of research are taken together, the big bang becomes by far the most convincing explanation of how the universe began, and is now accepted by almost all cosmologists. It has become the standard model of cosmology and also shows that, as the universe cooled, subatomic particles and atoms were formed in great clouds, and these were then brought together through gravitational pressure, to form galaxies and stars.

Opposite: This is a map showing the temperature variations in the cosmic microwave background, the radiation remaining from the big bang.

THE SINGULARITY AT THE START OF THE UNIVERSE

The identification of the cosmic microwave background may have promoted the big bang to its current status as the most widely accepted theory of how the universe began, but a number of serious issues remained – principal among these being the prediction, based on general relativity, that it started from a dot of infinite density. In the late 1960s Stephen Hawking and Roger Penrose addressed this problem by proposing that the big bang involved a singularity, a point where the normal laws of physics did not apply. What they were suggesting was that the beginning of the universe involved the reverse process to that which forms a black hole (in which a star collapses into itself with such massive gravitational pressure that nothing can escape from within it, including light).

Below: Stephen Hawking, one of the world's most widely recognised scientists, pictured here in 1979.

Hawking has since revised his views on this initial singularity, recognising that, as the universe began from an extremely small dot, it cannot be fully described through general relativity alone. Quantum effects also have to be taken into account. This can only

be achieved through a quantum theory of gravity (the search for which we encountered on page 148) and the potential outcome of such a resolution is impossible to know – not least because quantum gravity could predict an entirely different beginning for the universe, which does not include a big bang.

COSMIC INFLATION

The last major advance in our understanding of the big bang came in 1981, when Alan Guth, a cosmologist at the Massachusetts Institute of Technology, proposed the theory of cosmic inflation. This settled some of the unanswered questions that had arisen from research into the cosmic microwave background. A simple big bang with a uniform rate of expansion did not explain the observed geometric flatness of the universe when general relativity predicted it should be curved, and it did not account for its uniformity – or smoothness, as it is often called – where galaxies appear to be evenly distributed throughout the universe.

Guth envisaged that in the very first moments after the big bang there was an incredibly short period of accelerated expansion, which he called inflation, when the universe grew exponentially. After that, he thought the universe expanded at a slower rate, but inflation had, in effect, kick-started the expansion, so it grew to be much larger than what we can observe. Observing flatness in the cosmic microwave background is explained in similar terms to the effect of viewing the Earth as flat when looking at the horizon. The observable universe looks smooth for the same reason, because the initial burst of speed propelled galaxies out to the furthest points of the universe. So, however curved the universe may have been in its earliest stages, inflation ironed it out. The main problem with inflation is that little evidence supports it. We don't know how it started or why it stopped, and it seems we will have to wait to get a clear understanding of what exactly happened at the moment of the big bang – assuming, of course, there really was a big bang.

ALTERNATIVE THEORIES

Stephen Hawking once famously remarked that asking what came before the big bang is like asking what is north of the North Pole. According to the theory, space and time began with the big bang in the first place, so there can be no possibility of anything existing before it. An increasing number of cosmologists, though, have not been put off by the prospect of attempting to explain the inexplicable, and are prepared at least to think about what may have happened before the universe we live in existed.

One of these ideas has developed from the application of loop quantum gravity and describes a cycle of expansion and collapse, in which the present universe is one manifestation of a continuing process. In loop quantum cosmology, the big bang is replaced by a big bounce, in which the previous universe collapsed and contracted to a very small dot before entering an expansion phase. In his book *Seven Brief Lessons on Physics*, Carlo Rovelli writes that the

Above: It may look like gibberish to most of us, but equations form the basis of theoretical physics and cosmology.

big bounce is the moment when 'time and space have disappeared altogether, and the world has dissolved into a swarming cloud of probability which the equations can, however, still describe'. This means that no initial singularity would occur and the laws of physics are bent rather than broken. It has been suggested that evidence for this bounce could potentially be found in the cosmic microwave background or in gravitational waves, the ripples in space–time predicted by Einstein that have so far remained elusive.

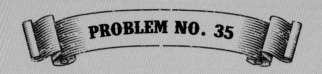
DOES THE MULTIVERSE EXIST?

Field: Theoretical cosmology
Location: In a different dimension

Proposing that our universe is not the only one used to be the quick route to career suicide for cosmologists, but times are changing and ideas about the multiverse are multiplying.

The idea that there are many universes, or even an infinite number, was strictly the territory of science-fiction writers, who were only constrained by their imaginations rather than the laws of physics, or by what was testable. Cosmologists confined themselves to studying what we can actually see within the observable universe using our most powerful telescopes. As the technology has advanced, we have been able to see further and further, so that now equipment like the Hubble Space Telescope can see almost as far as it is possible for light to have travelled since the early stages of the formation of the universe. This could be described as our cosmic visual horizon, but just as the horizon we can see when we are standing on land, looking out to sea, does not mark the end of the world, there is no reason to suppose that the cosmological horizon is the end of the universe either.

BEYOND THE HORIZON

In *The Restaurant at the End of the Universe*, Douglas Adams described the universe as being 'mind-bogglingly big', which is an easier way to think about it than attempting to comprehend the incredibly large numbers suggested by cosmologists, who have calculated its size from the rate of its expansion. It has been suggested that our observable universe is only one of an almost infinite number that exist in the vastness of space, each within their own bubbles of what can be observed, and each obeying the same laws of physics. If we think of all of these universes together then we arrive at what is sometimes called the patchwork multiverse, which forms the first level of four in the system of multiverse classification devised by Max Tegmark, professor of cosmology at the Massachusetts Institute of Technology and an enthusiastic proponent of the multiverse concept.

In level II, things become a little stranger because Tegmark describes this as containing a type of multiverse in which the

Below: Max Tegmark (left) attempting to explain himself to Mark Everett, Michio Kaku and Brian Cox.

laws of physics can vary between different universes, so that the nature of reality is not necessarily the same from one to another. The quantum world provides the setting for level III, in which the multiverse consists of universes that are constantly splitting to accommodate all the possible outcomes of quantum events. The final level encompasses all of the other levels and is Tegmark's own proposal for the multiverse, which he calls the mathematical universe hypothesis, and in which everything, including reality as we perceive it, consists of a mathematical structure. To describe this fully would require rather more space than we have here, so at this point it is probaby best to rcfer you to Tegmark's website and book, *The Mathematical Universe*, so that Max can explain his ideas to you himself.

ETERNAL INFLATION

Now that the concept of the multiverse no longer has to be discussed in the dark corners of university cosmology departments, a cottage industry of cosmologists has emerged, who all appear to have constructed their own pet theories. Many of these have been described as unscientific by critics of the multiverse concept because there can be no way of proving or disproving them. Eternal inflation, on the other hand, is one of the few that at least has the potential to be testable, even if our understanding of cosmological phenomena is not quite up to the job at the moment. It can be thought of as being an offshoot of the big bang theory, specifically of Alan Guth's proposal of cosmic inflation, and is based on the premise that, if inflation can happen once, then there is no reason why it could not happen on any number of occasions.

One version of this idea has been developed by Anthony Aguirre, professor of physics at the University of California, who suggests that multiple universes may exist as bubbles within the multiverse. Should our universe collide with one of the other bubbles, the consequences could persist in the cosmic microwave background and, as long as we know what we are looking for, it could then

ALTERNATIVE — THEORIES

One of the best-known examples of a level III multiverse is the many-worlds interpretation of quantum mechanics originally proposed by Hugh Everett in the 1950s. In a nutshell, this says that everything that can happen does happen in one of a very large number of quantum worlds, or parallel universes, as these are sometimes called. According to the theory, everything in the universe is subject to the principles of quantum mechanics, so objects have a probability of existing in more than one place at the same time, and the universe can split as many times as is necessary to accommodate all of these possibilities.

Above: A composite image of the centre of our own galaxy, the Milky Way – one very small part of the known universe.

It may sound like a sci-fi writer's dream, and we might lack any real evidence or solid methods to test this just yet, but you never know, it could just be true.

be detected. The map of the cosmic microwave background is becoming increasingly detailed, thanks to space telescopes, and it is not inconceivable, if, admittedly, not very likely, that an unexplained blemish could turn out to be the bruise left after two universes have bumped into each other. If no such bruise can be observed then the theory has been disproved, which will no doubt come as a blow to Aguirre, but will at least show that what he has been doing can be considered to have been science because his theory can be tested.

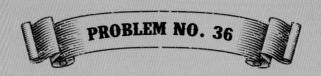
WHAT ARE DARK MATTER AND DARK ENERGY?

Field: Cosmology, astronomy, astrophysics,
theoretical physics, particle physics
Location: Everywhere, apparently

Despite a century of remarkable advances in cosmology, there are two enormous holes in the science, which, when taken together, mean that we don't have any idea what makes up 95 per cent of the universe.

These two unknowns have been given similar names, dark matter and dark energy, which may imply a relationship between them, though as far as we know they are completely separate. Both are referred to as dark because neither apparently emits light or any other form of electromagnetic radiation, such as X-rays, so we have no way of detecting their presence in the universe using telescopes or by any other means. What we can actually observe is what is known to physicists and cosmologists as baryonic matter, and what the rest of us may think of as ordinary matter, the stuff made of atoms – ourselves, the Earth, the Sun, the stars and everything else we can see.

The ordinary stuff adds up to about 5 per cent of the total mass of the universe, while dark matter contributes about 27 per cent.

All of the remaining 68 per cent is composed of dark energy, which is seemingly not matter but contributes to mass – in a form sometimes called 'energy density' – in accordance with $E=mc^2$, Einstein's mass–energy equivalence equation. All attempts to explain the unknown 95 per cent of the universe through what we already know have come to nothing. It has, for instance, nothing to do with the imbalance between the amounts of antimatter and matter in the universe, because we know that when antimatter is created it interacts with matter, causing both to be annihilated and releasing energy in the form of photons that we can detect.

It may be thought that black holes could at least contribute to the missing mass because, though composed of baryonic matter, no light or other electromagnetic radiation can escape from them, so we can't see them either. But the massive gravitational effects of black holes, which prevent light from escaping, also lead to interactions with other objects and cause detectable warps in space–time – and these have shown that, in any case, black holes have been far too few in number to make any significant contribution to accounting for the missing mass. Much the same can be said for other astronomical bodies that are either difficult or

Above: A distant galaxy known as El Gordo (the Fat One), most of the mass of which is made up of dark matter (indicated here in blue overlay).

Left: Jan Oort, photographed in 1975, whose observation led to the proposal of the presence of dark matter.

impossible to see, including neutron stars, white dwarfs and brown dwarfs, which are collectively known as massive astrophysical compact halo objects, or MACHOs for short. So, given our inability to see dark matter and dark energy, how can we go about finding out what each one actually is?

DARK MATTER

The first indication that we could not account for the total mass of the universe came in the early 1930s, through the observations of the Dutch astronomer Jan Oort, who had previously shown that the Sun is not at the centre of our own spiral galaxy, the Milky Way, and that the galaxy is rotating. Shortly afterwards, the Swiss astrophysicist Fritz Zwicky came to much the same conclusion from studies of more distant spiral galaxies, leading him to call undetectable material 'dark matter'. What they had both observed was that stars in distant orbits around the centre of spiral galaxies were moving at a much greater velocity than would be expected from the mass of the observable matter and its corresponding gravitational fields alone. If no other undetected matter were present then the speed of these stars should have caused them to

Opposite: The UK's Boulby Underground Laboratory, where attempts to detect dark matter are free from background interference.

shoot off into space, rather than remain in their orbits.

Some of the measurements and calculations made by Oort and Zwicky have since been shown to have been wrong, and it would be more than four decades before a detailed picture began to emerge from observations made by more powerful telescopes, and through analysis of the cosmic microwave background. But the principle they had established has been shown to be correct. It has become clear that dark matter, whatever it consists of, is present in the universe in very large quantities, and that nobody can account for it. Major research efforts in cosmology and physics are being undertaken to determine what all of this apparently invisible stuff is – principally through the use of particle accelerators, such as the Large Hadron Collider – on the assumption that it must be made of something. Attempts are also ongoing to devise ways of detecting the undetectable, directly or through any interactions it may have with other constituent parts of the observable universe.

Great success has been achieved in establishing the Standard Model of particle physics through proposing the existence of

hypothetical particles that have then been discovered by particle physicists – as with the Higgs boson – but to date this has not proved possible with dark matter. The two hypothetical particles attracting the most attention are axions and so-called weakly interacting massive particles (WIMPs). As well as using particle accelerators in an effort to create either of these particles, direct methods have also been employed, through setting up extremely sensitive equipment to detect them in deep mines, where the effects of cosmic rays are much weaker. So far, neither of these approaches has produced results, and indirect methods – such as attempting to detect any radiation given off by the hypothetical particles using space telescopes – have not fared any better.

DARK ENERGY

By the 1990s, observations of distant supernovae (immense and extremely bright explosions of stars) showed that the expansion of the universe was accelerating. At the time it was widely thought that the expansion should be slowing down rather than speeding up, as the gravitational attraction between the matter in the universe should act against the original kinetic energy of the big bang. Assuming the standard model of cosmology is correct, the only way of explaining the observed acceleration is that it was being caused by some other kind of energy than gravitation – one which repels rather than attracts – and, as nobody knows what this could be, it has become known as dark energy.

If anything, we know even less about dark energy than dark matter, because it is thought unlikely to be associated with any particles. So far, the only experimental progress has been the building of more powerful telescopes in order to observe supernovae in greater detail, in the hope that this will provide us with more information. A number of theoretical lines of research are being pursued, including what is known as the cosmological constant. This was originally proposed by Einstein in his equations for general relativity, at a time when the universe was thought

— ALTERNATIVE —
THEORIES

A theory which takes a different view on dark energy proposes that instead of it being the energy contained in the vacuum of space, described by the cosmological constant, it is in fact a fifth fundamental force to add to gravity, electromagnetic, strong nuclear and weak nuclear forces. Quintessence, as it has been called, is said to be a field that pervades the universe, as the cosmological constant does, but can vary with space and time. One obvious problem with the theory is that, as we can measure the other four forces, how come this one has eluded us? Theoretical physicists and cosmologists continue to scratch their heads.

Above: The remnants of the Cygnus Loop Nebula, one of the many supernovae that indicate the presence of dark energy in the universe.

to be static, in order to provide a counterbalance for gravity. When the universe was shown to be expanding in the 1920s, the constant was no longer required, and Einstein described using it as his greatest mistake. The cosmological constant provides a value for the energy density of the vacuum of space. This had been presumed to be zero, but, since we have become aware of dark energy, the constant has been reinstated – so that, though we don't know what dark energy is, it is accounted for in general relativity.

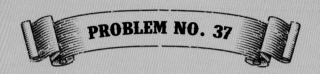

WHAT IS INSIDE A BLACK HOLE?

Field: Astrophysics, theoretical physics
Location: Beyond the event horizon

Black holes are one of the great enigmas of the cosmos. Since nothing can get out of them, not even light, it is impossible to look inside one to see what is happening.

In November 1783, a letter written by the Reverend John Michell, rector of the small town of Thornhill in the West Riding of Yorkshire, was read out at the Royal Society in London. In the letter, Michell set out his ideas concerning what he described as dark stars, which were based on Isaac Newton's theory of gravity and corpuscular theory of light. He calculated the size of gravitational pull that a star would need to exert in order to prevent light from reaching its required escape velocity, so that, rather than being emitted, the light is dragged back and the star becomes invisible. Michell anticipated Albert Einstein's thoughts about gravity's effects on light by more than a century, though by the late 1800s the speed of light had been shown to be constant.

A few months after Einstein's general theory of relativity was published in November 1915, Karl Schwarzschild provided solutions for what are known as Einstein's field equations, the

Left: A simulation of Sagittarius A*, a supermassive black hole thought to be at the centre of the Milky Way.

set of ten equations on which the theory was based. One of the outcomes of Schwarzschild's solutions was the prediction of black holes, though this did not become apparent until the 1930s, when it was worked out by a number of physicists – including Robert Oppenheimer, who would go on to lead the Manhattan Project to develop the first atomic bomb.

Einstein was never very comfortable with the central concept of the black hole: the gravitational singularity, in which gravity can become so immense in a star that is in the process of collapsing into itself that space–time becomes infinitely curved. As a consequence of this, nothing can escape a black hole's event horizon. This is the boundary at which gravitational pull becomes large enough to drag light – along with everything else, as nothing can travel faster than light – back into the hole. The only possible exception is known as Hawking radiation, predicted as being released from a black hole by Stephen Hawking in 1974, though this is yet to be confirmed. This all means that, as John Michell suggested, black holes cannot be directly observed – their existence

THE REGIONS OF A BLACK HOLE

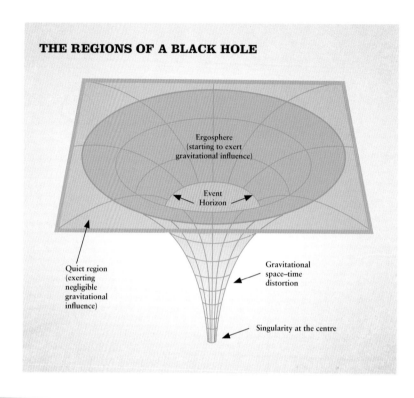

Ergosphere
(starting to exert
gravitational influence)

Event
Horizon

Quiet region
(exerting
negligible
gravitational
influence)

Gravitational
space–time
distortion

Singularity at the centre

Left: A diagram
illustrating the different
regions of a black hole,
according to current
understanding.

can only be inferred by indirect means, usually by detecting the
influence their huge gravitational field exerts on other objects in
space. In 1972, detection of an X-ray source emanating from the
Cygnus constellation of the Milky Way was thought to confirm
the discovery of the first black hole, named Cygnus-X1 – though
not everyone accepts these findings. It is now thought that
supermassive black holes are at the centre of most spiral galaxies,
including one named Sagittarius A* in the middle of the Milky
Way (see page 203).

ON THE INSIDE

As we can't even see a black hole, it is impossible to know for
certain what is inside one. Even if we could directly detect one, its
event horizon would present us with an impenetrable boundary.
Anything that is dragged into it by its gravitational pull would
become invisible to us, and could not re-emerge because it would

— ALTERNATIVE — THEORIES

In September 2014, Laura Mersini-Houghton, associate professor of theoretical physics at the University of North Carolina at Chapel Hill, produced mathematical proof that black holes do not exist. According to her work, as a star collapses under its own gravity and emits Hawking radiation, it must also lose mass, and, in doing so, cannot reach the density required for a singularity and an event horizon to form. Needless to say, this has not gone down well with those who make a living studying black holes, but then again, if theoretical physicists didn't have anything to argue about, then none of them would have a job in the first place.

Above: A Hubble Space Telescope image of the galaxy NGC 1097, thought to have a supermassive black hole at its centre.

have to achieve the impossible to do so: exceed the speed of light. This has led to the so-called black hole information paradox: general relativity indicates that everything falling into a black hole is effectively destroyed, including the physical information of that object, but a central tenet of quantum theory states that physical information is always preserved. In 2015, Stephen Hawking announced he had a possible solution to this paradox, suggesting the information could remain at the event horizon while the object fell in – though it is by no means clear how this could occur.

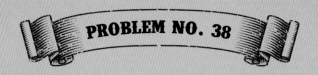

IS TIME TRAVEL POSSIBLE?

Field: Theoretical physics, mathematics, very theoretical cosmology
Location: In a time warp

Time travel has been used as a fictional plot device since H. G. Wells's novel *The Time Machine*, published in 1895, but can science shed any light on whether it is actually possible?

For his 70th birthday on 14 March 1949, Albert Einstein is said to have been given a newly worked-out solution to his field equations of general relativity by Kurt Gödel, his friend and colleague at Princeton University. Gödel is regarded as one of the outstanding mathematicians of the twentieth century, and Einstein is reported to have remarked in the later years of his academic career that he only continued to attend Princeton in order to have the privilege of walking to and from work with him. However highly Einstein regarded his friend, though, he may not have been overly delighted by Gödel's present, because he was not always very receptive to some of the stranger applications of his theory – and his friend's work contained a solution which suggested that time travel was possible.

The solution, known as the Gödel metric, showed that the universe could be rotating and, if this were the case, then space–time could bend back upon itself to create loops in which time continually repeated itself. In physics, this is known as a 'closed timelike curve'. If it were possible to travel along one of these curves, then in theory we would be transported back in time. Einstein appears to have been sufficiently worried about these implications to address Gödel's work, stating that such loops in space–time may be a mathematical possibility, but this did not conform to the physical reality of the universe.

Though, as we have already found (see page 186), there is plenty of observable evidence to show that the universe is expanding, there is nothing to suggest that it is also rotating. Gödel himself does not appear to have thought that time travel was possible in this way and, in any case, he used a high value for the cosmological constant in solving the equations in a way that led to a rotating universe. Nevertheless, he provided science-fiction writers with an opportunity to justify the use of time travel in their work, should they feel the need to do so, because Einstein's theory of general relativity, the backbone of modern physics, showed that it was theoretically possible.

Below: Kurt Gödel (left) and Albert Einstein at Princeton University. The two often walked to work together.

WORMHOLES

One concept most of us who have watched sci-fi movies will have encountered at one time or another is wormholes – on screen this usually involves a spaceship voyaging through one such hole, accompanied by some swirling lights and vortices, before emerging

Above: The astronomer Carl Sagan (centre), who sparked a whole new field of research after using the concept of time travel through wormholes in a science-fiction novel.

in some distant part of the universe or at some point in the past or future. In that classic of the slacker movie genre, *Bill & Ted's Excellent Adventure*, for instance, the eponymous heroes travel in a time machine through a wormhole, back to a variety of places in the past, so that they can assemble a cast of famous historical figures to help them with their history reports.

It is hard to imagine what Einstein would have made of Bill and Ted's use of wormholes, though it was a concept that he had actually considered himself. In a paper written in 1935 with physicist Nathan Rosen, he addressed an issue that had originally emerged in 1916 from Karl Schwarzschild's solutions to the field equations of general relativity, answering this by suggesting the possibility of tubes or bridges in space–time, brought about if gravitational effects were strong enough for sufficiently large curvatures to form. These Einstein–Rosen bridges would occur where space–time had effectively curved back in on itself and the resulting tubes could then connect to other regions of the universe.

No Einstein–Rosen bridges have so far been detected in space, but we can nevertheless conjecture that, if it were possible to travel through one, we could get to a distant part of the universe faster than the speed of light, and, if we could do that, then as well as travel across immense distances, time travel would also become possible. Einstein did not address these possibilities in his work, but the well-known cosmologist Carl Sagan used the

— ALTERNATIVE —
THEORIES

Stephen Hawking has been rather more open to engaging with the concept of time travel than Einstein was – though, of course, it is not one of his theories that is being messed with. He thinks that, if anything, we will only be able to go into the future, citing the so-called grandfather paradox as a reason why we could not go back to the past. This describes a situation in which a time traveller attempts to kill his own grandfather before he had met the woman who will become the time traveller's grandmother. If the murder is successful, it would mean that the traveller would never have existed, so could not have gone back in time to kill his grandfather.

Above: The grandfather paradox explains why going back in time to kill your own grandfather is a bad idea.

idea of Einstein–Rosen bridges as a device in his science-fiction novel *Contact*, first published in 1985, in which he envisaged that wormholes could be used as shortcuts between distant parts of the universe. Since then, such wormholes have been used in all sorts of films, some more serious than others, but unfortunately, back in the real world, actual time travel continues to elude us. It remains entirely theoretical so, if we ever do find a wormhole, I for one won't be volunteering to be the first to travel through it.

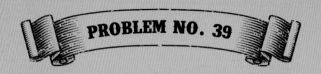

PROBLEM NO. 39

DOES EXTRATERRESTRIAL LIFE EXIST?

Field: Cosmology, astrobiology
Location: Across the universe

As far as we know, the Earth is the only place in the universe where life exists, but we have long been intrigued by the possibility that we are not alone.

If we start with the premise that any extraterrestrial life that exists in the universe has developed in a similar way to life on Earth, the obvious place to begin looking is as close to home as possible. So far nothing resembling life has been found on the Moon, which has almost no atmosphere, and Venus, sometimes called our sister planet, has a surface temperature of over 450°C (840°F) and an atmosphere composed mostly of carbon dioxide, containing thick clouds of sulphuric acid. Mars could hardly be described as possessing ideal conditions for life to thrive, but it is by no means as inhospitable as Venus. While it is much colder than Earth, with a thin atmosphere, also mostly of carbon dioxide, the surface is dusty and desert-like, its reddish colour caused by large powdered iron oxide minerals in the dust. The planet lacks a magnetic field to shield it from solar wind and cosmic rays, which has meant that a thicker atmosphere has not developed and, though there is evidence of there having been liquid water on its

surface in the past, any that has not been locked in its polar ice caps appears to have evaporated away into space.

In September 2015, NASA announced that its Mars Reconnaissance Orbiter had confirmed earlier indications of the presence of flowing salty water, either on or just below the surface of the planet. Features described as recurring slope lineae, which are dark streaks running down a sloping feature in the Martian landscape, are thought to have been caused by the seasonal flow of water, which contains enough salt to be liquid in the warmest parts of the Martian year. The presence of water on its own does not necessarily mean that life exists on the planet, but it at least shows that some of the conditions required for life are present. NASA already has two rovers (*Opportunity* and *Curiosity*) on the surface of Mars, and plans to send another in 2020 to land in the vicinity of the streaks, which it will test for signs of life.

Above: Clay minerals and a delta deposit in the Jezero Crater region of Mars indicate that water, essential for life on Earth, once flowed here.

THE GOLDILOCKS ZONE

Should we ever find life on Mars, it will almost certainly be in its simplest unicellular form, so to look for intelligent life, should it exist, we will have to search much further afield. If we discount the numerous conspiracy theories that argue that extraterrestrials have been found on Earth and our governments are keeping the details from us, then we currently have no evidence to suggest that there is anything out there we could start a conversation with – but if we consider the enormous size of the universe, then the possibility cannot be entirely discounted. The observable universe consists of about 200 billion galaxies and there are estimated to be 500 billion stars, and quite possibly very many more, in our own relatively modest Milky Way alone.

Observing distant planets is difficult, because they are obscured by light emitted from the stars that they are orbiting. So we have no idea how many planets are out there, but of the multiple billions that must surely

Above: The Green Bank Telescope in West Virginia, the largest steerable radio telescope in the world.

exist, a proportion must be in the so-called Goldilocks zone, the relatively narrow region around a star within which conditions of temperature and pressure are potentially just right to support life. In 2013, astronomers studying data from NASA's Kepler space observatory – launched in 2009 specifically to look for habitable Earth-like planets – announced that there could be as many as 40 billion within the Goldilocks zone in the Milky Way, though it is impossible to know how many of them fulfil all the other criteria required for life.

One approach to investigating the possible presence of intelligent life is to use radio telescopes to search for extraterrestrial signals. Various SETI ('search for extraterrestrial intelligence') projects have been set up, prominent among them the SETI Institute in Mountain View, California, and these have been scanning the skies for decades without success. In 2015, Stephen Hawking was one of the prominent scientists to announce the so-called Breakthrough

— ALTERNATIVE — THEORIES

At about 10.15 on the evening of 15 August 1977, a SETI project using Ohio State University's Big Ear radio telescope to search for radio signals from space appeared to have hit the jackpot, when a very strange reading appeared on the telescope's printout. Jerry Ehman, the astronomer on duty that night, circled it using a red pen and wrote 'Wow!' in the margin. Now known as the Wow! signal, this did not come from within our solar system, though the exact location has proved difficult to establish. It remains unexplained today, but if it really was aliens attempting to contact us, they never tried it again. Maybe they thought we were being rude by not replying.

Above: The Perkins Observatory, where Ohio State University's Big Ear radio telescope picked up the Wow! signal.

Initiatives, a plan funded by Russian billionaire businessman and physicist Yuri Milner to devote thousands of hours of radio telescope time to the search, at the Parkes Observatory in Australia and the Green Bank Telescope in America, two of the most powerful in the world. It is by far the biggest SETI project ever attempted, so any shy ETs hiding out there should be worried, because they now have Stephen Hawking on their case.

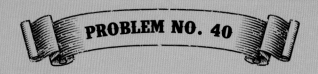
WHAT IS THE FATE OF THE UNIVERSE?

Field: Theoretical cosmology, physical cosmology
Location: Here, there and everywhere

If the standard model of cosmology is correct, then the universe started with the big bang. But, if it had a beginning, does that mean it must also come to an end?

It now appears to be an unwritten law of physics that the name given to any theory concerning the end of the universe that arises from the big bang proposition must also have the word 'big' in its name. We have already encountered the big bounce (see page 191), which suggests that the universe is in a constant cycle of expansion and collapse, so that it never actually comes to an end, and here we will consider a few other theories cosmologists have put forward to explain how the universe will end in a big way.

The big crunch has some similarities to the big bounce, except, as the name suggests, it is rather more final. It suggests that the universe will eventually come to an end in a similar fashion to the way a massive star dies, which occurs when its density rises, after it has burnt all of the hydrogen in its core and begins to burn helium instead. This results in the production of heavier elements, causing a rise in density and an accompanying increase in its

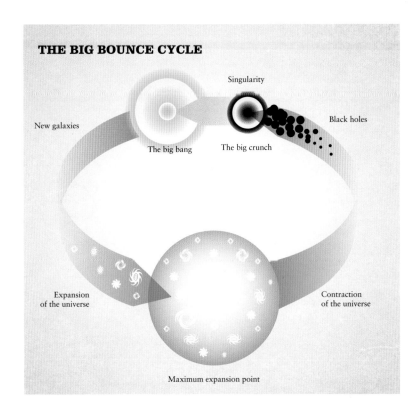

THE BIG BOUNCE CYCLE

New galaxies

The big bang

Singularity

The big crunch

Black holes

Expansion
of the universe

Contraction
of the universe

Maximum expansion point

Left: A diagram illustrating the big bounce cycle. In both the big bounce and big crunch theories, the universe collapses into itself after reaching its maximum extent

gravitational pull, until this pull becomes so strong that the star collapses into itself to form a black hole. In the big crunch, the gravity of all the matter in the universe will eventually cause it to stop expanding and, when that happens, it will collapse back into itself until it forms the same sort of singularity that is at the heart of a black hole. In the big bounce scenario, the universe begins to expand again before reaching the point of the singularity, but in the big crunch all the matter in the universe is crunched up into nothing and that is the end of the story.

THE BIG RIP

The discovery in the 1990s that the expansion of the universe was not slowing down but accelerating created a big problem for the big crunch, and has also led to the development of the big rip. In this scenario the acceleration continues, so that the universe expands at an ever-increasing rate until it reaches a critical point at which it tears itself apart. Galaxies will be stretched until they are torn apart, followed by much the same thing happening to every solar system, and then stars, planets and all other matter will become separated into their constituent atoms, before finally the atoms themselves will be ripped apart, until there is nothing left. Some of the cosmologists who support this theory have had enough confidence in it to give it a timescale, saying that it will take place in 22 billion years' time, give or take a few billion. The problem with this theory is that it relies on the prediction that the acceleration will continue indefinitely, and this will be determined by the properties of dark energy. We known absolutely nothing about this elusive force and, until we do, it is rather difficult to determine whether the big rip theory makes any sort of sense.

HEAT DEATH

Another idea applies the laws of thermodynamics to the expanding universe, to show that it will eventually undergo so-called heat death. This may sound like a proposition that the universe will burn itself up, but it actually means the opposite, in that it suggests the future death of heat. As the universe expands, matter will move increasingly far apart, and, as the second law of thermodynamics states, entropy always increases – meaning that heat will gradually spread out to become uniform, so that no energy is being exchanged and no work is done. The average temperature of the universe, which is slightly above absolute zero, will prevail everywhere, leading some cosmologists to give this theory the inevitable title of the big freeze.

If this all sounds like we have a bleak future mapped out, it may be worth remembering that, at least according to some cosmologists, the universe has another 20 billion years or so left, so we don't need to get too worried just yet. In any case, before any bounce, crunch, rip or freeze occurs, our Sun will have long since run out of hydrogen. As it burns helium, and then the heavier elements

— ALTERNATIVE —
THEORIES

To end on a rather more optimistic note, the theory of rainbow gravity, presumably named by a Thomas Pynchon fan, suggests that the universe did not begin with a big bang, and that time extends indefinitely into the past. Apparently this has something to do with the way gravity affects different wavelengths of light, though why this should be the case is by no means clear. But it also implies that, as there was no beginning, there will be no end. Not too many cosmologists give this theory the time of day, but if it turns out to be correct, then we have nothing to worry about. The universe will continue to muddle along as it always has.

Above: According to rainbow gravity, the end of the universe is, like the end of a rainbow, a place that can never be reached.

that are formed, it will expand to become a red giant, which will engulf the Earth, swallowing it into its fiery inferno. This won't happen for another six or seven billion years, but, even so, perhaps we should make best use of whatever time we have left.

FURTHER READING

BOOKS

Al-Khalili, Jim, and Johnjoe McFadden. *Life on the Edge: The Coming of Age of Quantum Biology.* London: Bantam Press, 2014.

Calder, Nigel. *Magic Universe: The Oxford Guide to Modern Science.* Oxford: Oxford University Press, 2003.

Carey, Nessa. *The Epigenetics Revolution: How Modern Biology is Rewriting Our Understanding of Genetics, Disease and Inheritance.* London: Icon Books, 2011.

Cox, Brian, and Jeff Forshaw. *The Quantum Universe: Everything That Can Happen Does Happen.* London: Allen Lane, 2011.

Dorling, Danny. *Population 10 Billion: The Coming Demographic Crisis and How to Survive It.* London: Constable, 2013.

Eggleton, Tony. *A Short Introduction to Climate Change.* Cambridge: Cambridge University Press, 2012.

Ferreira, Pedro G. *The Perfect Theory: A Century of Geniuses and Battle Over General Relativity.* London: Little Brown, 2014.

Feynman, Richard. *QED: The Strange Theory of Light and Matter.* Princeton, New Jersey: Princeton University Press, 1985.

Fortey, Richard. *The Earth: An Intimate History.* London: Harper Collins, 2004.

Gould, James L., and Carol Grant Gould. *Nature's Compass: The Mysteries of Animal Navigation.* Princeton: Princeton University Press, 2012.

Gould, Stephen Jay. *Wonderful Life: The Burgess Shale and the Nature of History.* London: Hutchinson Radius, 1990.

Kandel, Eric. *In Search of Memory: The Emergence of a New Science of Mind.* London: W. W. Norton, 2007.

Koslow, Tony. *The Silent Deep: The Discovery, Ecology and Conservation of the Deep Sea.* Chicago: University of Chicago Press, 2007.

Lane, Nick. *The Vital Question: Why is Life the Way it is?* London: Profile Books, 2015.

Liddle, Andrew, and Jon Loveday. *The Oxford Companion to Cosmology.* Oxford: Oxford University Press, 2008.

Martin, Paul. *Counting Sheep: The Science and Pleasures of Sleep and Dreams.* London: Harper Collins, 2002.

McManus, Chris. *Right Hand, Left Hand: The Origins of Asymmetry in Brains, Bodies, Atoms and Cultures.* London: Weidenfeld and Nicolson, 2002.

Mukherjee, Siddharth. *The Emperor of All Maladies: A Biography of Cancer.* London: Fourth Estate, 2011.

Pinker, Steven. *The Language Instinct: How the Mind Creates Language.* New York: William Morrow and Company, 1994.

Rovelli, Carlo. *Seven Brief Lessons on Physics.* London: Allen Lane, 2015.

Tegmark, Max. *The Mathematical Universe: My Quest for the Nature of Reality.* London: Allen Lane, 2014.

Weinberg, Steven. *To Explain the World: The Discovery of Modern Science.* London: Allen Lane, 2015.

Wilczek, Frank. *A Beautiful Question: Finding Nature's Deep Design.* London: Allen Lane, 2015.

WEBSITES

The Breakthrough Initiatives
breakthroughinitiatives.org

Gapminder: Unveiling the Beauty of Statistics for a Fact-based Worldview
gapminder.org

The Intergovernmental Panel on Climate Change
ipcc.ch

The International Thermonuclear Experimental Reactor
iter.org

London South Bank University. 'Water Structure and Science.'
lsbu.ac.uk/water/water_structure_science.html

NASA
nasa.gov

Nature
nature.com

New Scientist
newscientist.com

The Royal Society
royalsociety.org

The Science Museum
sciencemuseum.org.uk

Scientific American
scientificamerican.com

The SETI Institute
seti.org

The Smithsonian
si.edu

Stephen Hawking
hawking.org.uk

The Universes of Max Tegmark
space.mit.edu/home/tegmark/home

The US National Academy of Sciences
nasonline.org

The World Health Organization
who.int

INDEX

IMAGE CREDITS